math
expressions

Dr. K

S0-BZO-373

Assessment Guide | Grade K

This material is based upon work supported by the
National Science Foundation
under Grant Numbers
ESI-9816320, REC-9806020, and RED-935373.

Any opinions, findings, and conclusions, or recommendations expressed in this material
are those of the author and do not necessarily reflect the views of the National Science Foundation.

HMH

Printed in the U.S.A.

ISBN   978-1-328-70362-0

1 2 3 4 5 6 7 8 9 10   1026   26 25 24 23 22 21 20 19 18 17

4500662868   B C D E F G

© Houghton Mifflin Harcourt Publishing Company

Prerequisite Skill	DoK	Item Number	Last Name, First Name											
understands the relationship between numbers and quantities	2	1												
understands the relationship between numbers and quantities	2	2												
writes numerals from 0 to 20	1	3												
represents a number of objects with a numeral	2	4												
represents a number of objects with a numeral	2	5												
understands number of objects is the same regardless of arrangement	2	6												
understands number of objects is the same regardless of arrangement	2	7												
identifies groups that are greater than, less than, or equal to	2	8												

Prerequisite Skill	DoK	Item Number	Last Name, First Name												
identifies groups that are greater than, less than, or equal to	1	9													
identifies groups that are greater than, less than, or equal to	1	10													
solves addition and subtraction word problems using objects	1	11													
solves addition and subtraction word problems using objects	1	12													
solves addition and subtraction word problems using objects	1	13													
identifies groups that are greater than, less than, or equal to	2	14													
decomposes numbers less than or equal to 10	1	15													
for any number from 1 to 9, find the number that makes 10	1	16													

Prerequisite Skill	DoK	Item Number	Last Name, First Name												
directly compares two objects with measurable attributes	1	17													
directly compares two objects with measurable attributes	1	18													
classifies objects into different categories	2	19													
analyzes and compares shapes	1	20													
correctly names shapes	1	21													
correctly names shapes	1	22													
correctly names shapes regardless of orientation	1	23													
models shapes in the world	1	24													
analyzes and com-pares shapes using informal language	1	25													

Counting and Cardinality

1 Count the tiger cubs.

Circle how many.

3   4   5

---

2 Count the eggs in the nest.
Circle how many.

4   3   2

3 Circle the number seven.

$$5 \qquad 6 \qquad 7$$

---

4 Circle the number that tells how many.

$$3 \qquad 4 \qquad 5$$

---

5 Circle the number that tells how many.

$$6 \qquad 7 \qquad 8$$

6 Circle the groups of 9 dots.

---

7 Circle the groups of 4 dots.

8 Circle the group that has more.

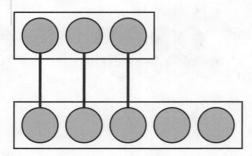

---

9 Count each group.
Circle the group that has less.

Operations and Algebraic Thinking

10 Circle the group that has one more apple.

---

11 How many kittens in all?
Write the number.

12 How many circles in all?
Write the number.

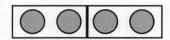

13 Circle the group that has one less frog.

14 Count and circle the number that is less.

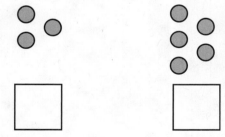

Number and Operations in Base Ten

15 Circle the group that shows 10.

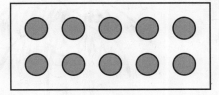

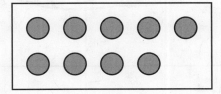

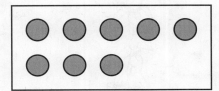

16 Draw extra dots to show 10.

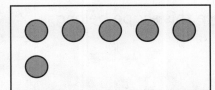

Measurement and Data

17 Circle the trees that are the same.

18 Circle the taller plant.

19 Circle the group where this shape belongs.

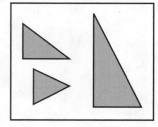   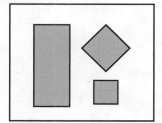

Geometry

20 Circle the shape that is round.

---

21 Circle the triangle.

---

22 Circle the square.

23 Circle the shape that is like this shape.

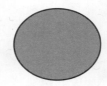 

---

24 Circle the shape that is shaped like a can of paint.

 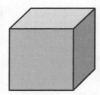

---

25 How many sides does this shape have?
Circle how many.

2   3   4

CCSS	DoK	Item Number	Last Name, First Name														
K.CC.A.1	1	1															
K.CC.A.2	1	2															
K.CC.A.3	2	3															
K.CC.B.4.A	1	4															
K.CC.B.4.B	2	5															
K.CC.B.4.C	2	6															
K.CC.B.5	1	7															
K.CC.C.6	2	8															
K.CC.C.7	2	9															
K.CC.C.7	2	10															
K.OA.A.3	1	11															
K.OA.A.5	1	12															
K.OA.A.2	2	13															
K.OA.A.3	2	14															
K.OA.A.4	1	15															
K.OA.A.5	1	16															
K.OA.A.5	1	17															
K.NBT.A.1	2	18															

CCSS	DoK	Item Number	Last Name, First Name													
K.NBT.A.1	1	19														
K.NBT.A.1	1	20														
K.MD.A.1	2	21														
K.MD.A.2	2	22														
K.MD.B.3	2	23														
K.G.A.1	2	24														
K.G.A.2	1	25														
K.G.A.3	1	26														
K.G.A.3	1	27														
K.G.B.4	1	28														
K.G.B.4	1	29														
K.G.B.6	2	30														

Counting and Cardinality

1 Write the missing numbers from 1 to 10.

1									10

2 Circle the numbers that are in counting order.

1 5 3 7

4 3 5 6

2 3 4 5

3 How many cars? Write the number.

4 Circle the numbers that are in order when counting this group.

1, 2, 3, 4

1, 2, 4, 5

1, 2, 3, 5

---

5 Circle the number you say last when counting this group.

5   6   7

6 Circle the number that comes next.

3   4

○○○○
○○○

7

○○○
○○○

6

○○○
○○

5

---

7 Circle the group of 6 cats.

8 Circle the group that has more.

5

3

Compare the numbers.
Write G for **Greater than** or L for **Less than.**

9

| 2 | _____ | 5 |

10

| 9 | _____ | 3 |

Operations and Algebraic Thinking

11 Write the partners.

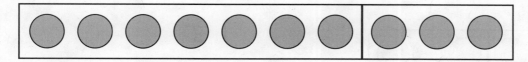

$$10 = \boxed{} + \boxed{}$$

---

12 Subtract the numbers.

$$4 - 2 = \boxed{}$$

---

13 There are 4 butterflies on a bush.
Then 3 butterflies fly away. How many butterflies are
left on the bush? Write the equation.

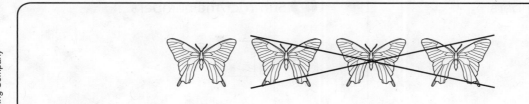

Equation: _____ – _____ = _____

14 Write the partners.

5

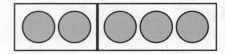

☐ + ☐

---

15 Write the partners.

10 = ☐ + ☐

---

16 Add the numbers.

2 + 2 = ☐

17 Subtract the numbers.

4 − 1 = ☐

Number and Operations in Base Ten

 Circle a group of 10. Write how many in all.

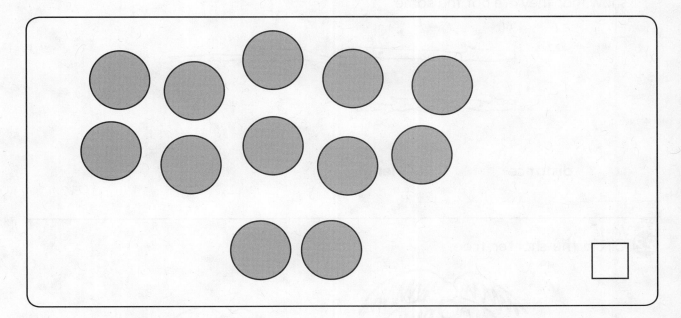

Write the total.

$$10 + 3 = \boxed{}$$

20

$$\boxed{} = 10 + 8$$

Measurement and Data

21 Circle the word that tells how the branches could be compared to show that they are not the same.

distance   length   time

---

22 Circle the shorter tree.

---

23 Count the squares and circles.
Circle the number that is more.

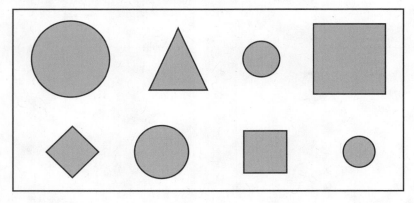

Name _____ Date _____

Geometry

24 Circle the sphere that is beside the cube.

---

25 Circle the triangle.

---

26 Circle the flat shape.

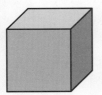

---

27 Circle the solid shape.

© Houghton Mifflin Harcourt Publishing Company

28 Circle the shape that is like the first shape.

 |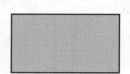

---

29 Circle the shape that is shaped like a party hat.

---

30 Meg stacks a cone and a cube.

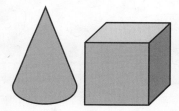

Circle the new shape that she makes.

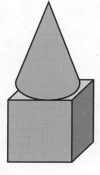 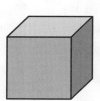 

CCSS		DoK	Item Number	Last Name, First Name											
K.CC.B.5	K.CC.4.B	—	1												
K.CC.B.5	K.CC.4.B	—	2												
K.CC.B.5	K.CC.4.B	—	3												
K.CC.B.5	K.CC.4.B	—	4												
	K.G.A.2	2	5												
	K.G.A.2	2	6												
	K.CC.A.2	—	7												
	K.CC.A.2	—	8												
	K.CC.A.3	—	9												
	K.CC.B.5	2	10												
K.G.A.2	K.CC.B.5	3	11												

© Houghton Mifflin Harcourt Publishing Company

Ring groups of the number.

Mark an X on the groups that are not the number.

1 3

2 |

---

3 Draw 4 apples.

4 Draw 2 fish.

5 Draw a line under each circle.

6 Draw a line under each rectangle.

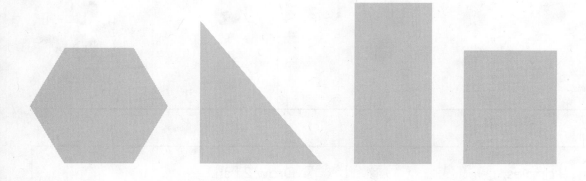

Connect the dots in order.

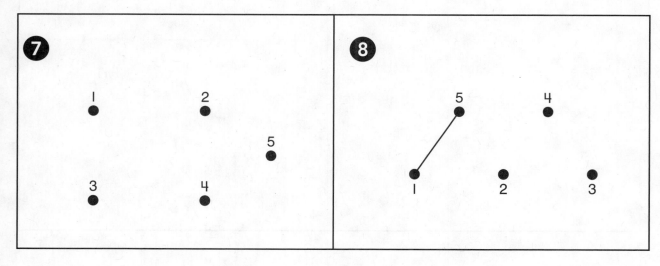

9 Write the numbers.

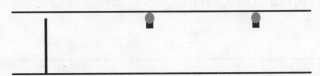

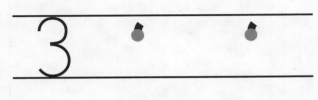

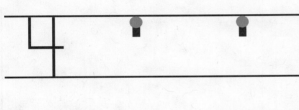

---

10 Does the picture match the number? Choose Yes or No.

         ○ Yes   ○ No

Make a drawing. Use 1 rectangle, 2 squares, and 4 circles.
Did you draw fewer rectangles or squares? Mark an X on the
shape that has fewer.

CCSS	DoK	Item Number	Last Name, First Name												
K.CC.A.3	1	1													
K.CC.A.3	1	2													
K.CC.4.B K.CC.B.5	2	3													
K.G.A.2	1	4													
K.CC.A.2	2	5													
K.CC.A.3	1	6													
K.G.A.2 K.CC.B.5	2	7													
K.CC.A.2 K.CC.B.5	1	8													
K.G.A.2	2	9													
K.CC.B.5	2	10													

Fill in the ◯ for the correct answer.

Which group shows the number?

1 5   ◯    ◯    ◯

2 4   ◯   ◯   ◯

3 Which group shows 5 pails?

◯

◯

◯

4 Which shape is a circle?

○   ○ ■   ○ ⬠

---

5 Which shows the dots connected in order?

○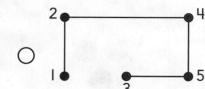

○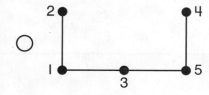

○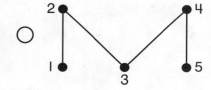

6 Which shows how to write the number four?

○ 2

○ 3

○ 4

7 Which group has 3 squares and 4 circles?

○

○

○

8 Draw 2 buttons.

9 Draw a line under each square.

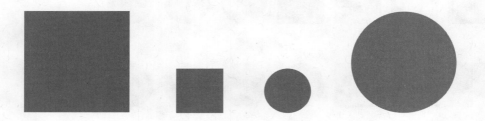

10 Connect the dots in order.

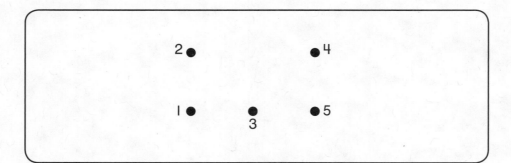

Name _____   Date _____

Count on It

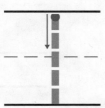

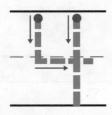

DIRECTIONS 1. Trace each number. Draw balloons to show that number.
Circle the number that is 1 larger than 4.

Name _____ Date _____

 2

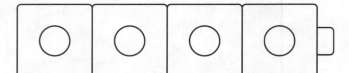

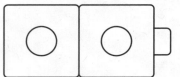

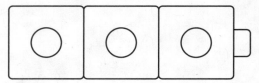

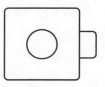

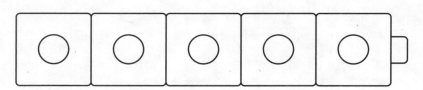

3 _____

- - - - - - - - - - - - - -

_____

DIRECTIONS **2.** Count the cubes in each set. Write that number of cubes.
3. Write the numbers in order at the bottom of the page.

Addition Concepts

Count on It

COMMON CORE STANDARDS

K.CC.A.3 Write numbers from 0 to 20. Represent a number of objects with a written numeral 0–20 (with 0 representing a count of no objects).

K.CC.B.4.A When counting objects, say the number names in the standard order, pairing each object with one and only one number name and each number name with one and only one object.

K.CC.B.4.B Understand that the last number name said tells the number of objects counted. The number of objects is the same regardless of their arrangement or the order in which they were counted.

K.CC.B.4.C Understand that each successive number name refers to a quantity that is one larger.

PURPOSE

To assess the ability to model, count, and write numbers to 5 and to understand that each successive number refers to a quantity that is one larger.

ESTIMATED TIME

25–30 minutes

GROUPING

Individuals

MATERIALS

- Copy of the task for each student, paper, pencil
- Connecting cubes (optional)

PREPARATION HINTS

- Review counting sets of objects to 5 with children before assigning the task.
- Review written numerals 0–5 with children before assigning the task.
- Review vocabulary, including *zero, one, two, three, four, five, larger*.

IMPLEMENTATION NOTES

- Read the task aloud to children and make sure that all children have a clear understanding of the task.
- Children may use manipulatives to complete the task.
- Allow children as much paper as they need to complete the task.
- Allow as much time as children need to complete the task.
- Children must complete the task individually, without collaboration.
- Collect all work when the task is complete.

TASK SUMMARY

Children use understanding of cardinality to model, count, and write numerals to represent quantities up to 5. They identify a number that is 1 larger than a given number and write numerals in standard order.

REPRESENTATION

In this task teachers can...

- Provide options for language, mathematical expressions, and symbols by illustrating examples of terms used in directions.
- Provide options for comprehension by highlighting the relationship between numeric and pictorial representations.

ACTION and EXPRESSION

In this task teachers can...

- Provide options for physical action by allowing varied methods of response depending on motor skills.
- Provide options for physical action by offering connecting cubes to students while completing the task.

ENGAGEMENT

In this task teachers can...

- Sustain effort and persistence by providing specific feedback.

EXPECTED STUDENT OUTCOMES

- Reflect engagement in a productive struggle
- Model, count, write, and order numbers to 5

SCORING

Use the associated rubric to evaluate each child's work.

COUNT ON IT

Problem #	Points
The student:	
1. • draws the correct number of balloons	2
• circles 5	1
2. • counts the cubes accurately	1
• writes the corresponding number for the cubes	2
3. • writes the numbers correctly	1
• writes the numbers in order	1
TOTAL POINTS:	8

Point Score and equivalent Performance Level
(see rubrics below):

   7–8 points = Level 3

   5–6 points = Level 2

   3–4 points = Level 1

   1–2 points = Level 0

COUNT ON IT

A level 3 response	• Indicates that the child has made sense of the task and persevered • Demonstrates an understanding of the relationship between numerals and the quantities they represent • Indicates an understanding that the last number name said tells the number of objects counted • Demonstrates an understanding that each successive number refers to a quantity that is one larger
A level 2 response	• Indicates that the child has made sense of the task and persevered • Demonstrates an understanding of the relationship between numerals and the quantities they represent • Indicates an understanding that the last number name said tells the number of objects counted • Demonstrates an understanding that each successive number refers to a quantity that is one larger • Addresses most or all aspects of the task, but there may be errors of omission
A level 1 response	• Shows that the child has made sense of at least some elements of the task • Shows evidence of understanding the relationship between numerals and quantities and that the last number name said tells the number of objects counted • May not indicate an understanding that each successive number refers to a quantity that is one larger • May contain errors in counting or in writing numerals
A level 0 response	• Shows little evidence that the child has made sense of the problems of the task • Reflects lack of understanding of the relationship between numerals and quantities • Shows little evidence of addressing the elements of the task

Sample Level 3 Response

Unit 1 Performance Assessment

Name ______________________ Date __________

Count on It

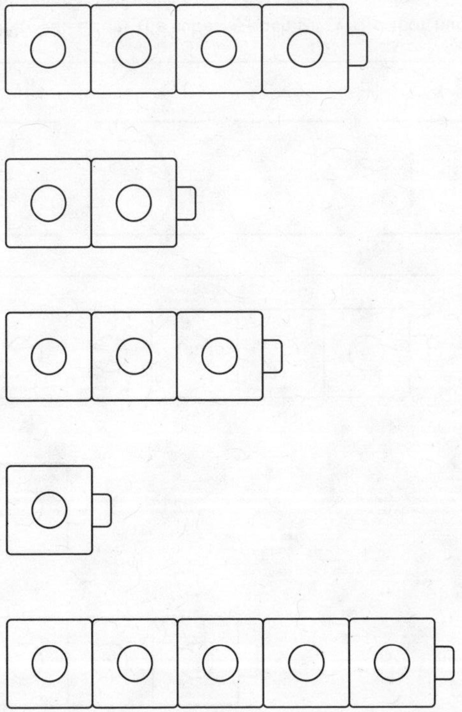

1

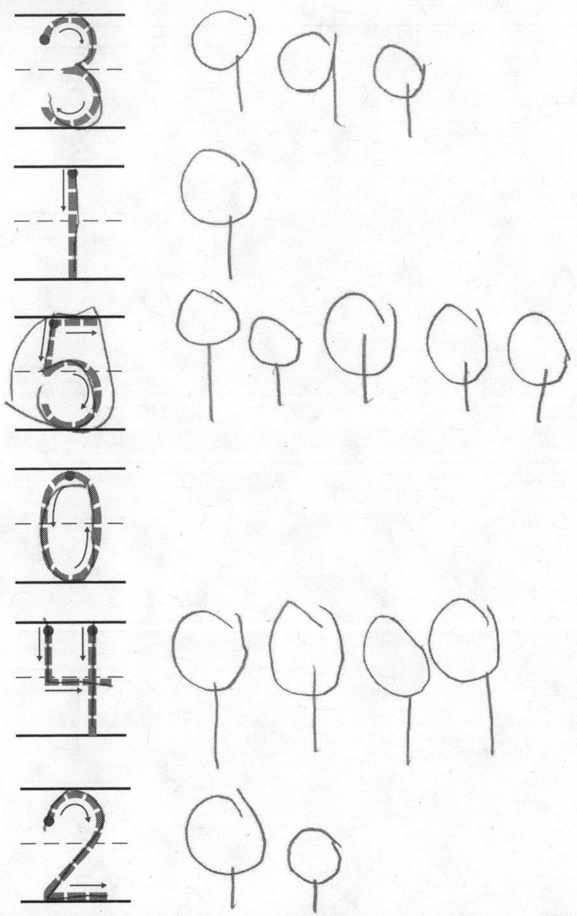

DIRECTIONS 1. Trace each number. Draw balloons to show that number. Circle the number that is 1 larger than 4.

Name ______________________ Date __________

2

4 2 3 1 5

3

1 2 3 4 5

DIRECTIONS 2. Count the cubes in each set. Write that number of cubes. 3. Write the numbers in order at the bottom of the page.

Name _____

Date _____

2

H 4 3 1 5

3

1 2 3 4 5

DIRECTIONS 2. Count the cubes in each set. Write that number of cubes.
3. Write the numbers in order at the bottom of the page.

Name _____

Date _____

Count on It

1

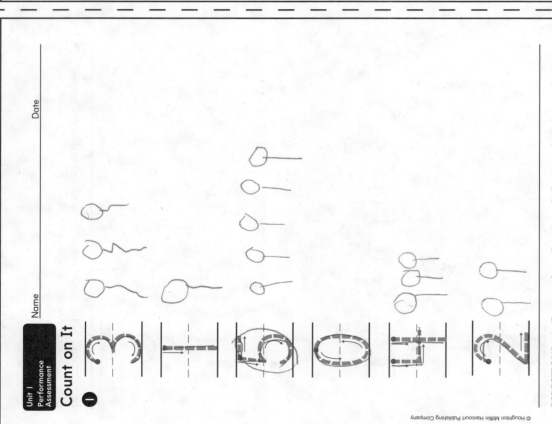

3   1   5   0   4   2

DIRECTIONS 1. Trace each number. Draw balloons to show that number.
Circle the number that is 1 larger than 4.

© Houghton Mifflin Harcourt Publishing Company

Name _____ Date _____

2

3

3 2 3 1

DIRECTIONS 2. Count the cubes in each set. Write that number of cubes.
3. Write the numbers in order at the bottom of the page.

© Houghton Mifflin Harcourt Publishing Company

Name _____ Date _____

Unit 1
Performance
Assessment

Count on It

1

DIRECTIONS 1. Trace each number. Draw balloons to show that number.
Circle the number that is 1 larger than 4.

© Houghton Mifflin Harcourt Publishing Company

DIRECTIONS 2. Count the cubes in each set. Write that number of cubes.
3. Write the numbers in order at the bottom of the page.

Name _____ Date _____

Unit 1
Performance
Assessment

Count on It

DIRECTIONS 1. Trace each number. Draw balloons to show that number.
Circle the number that is 1 larger than 4.

Name _____ Date _____

CCSS		DoK	Item Number	Last Name, First Name											
	K.CC.B.5	1	1												
	K.CC.B.5	1	2												
K.CC.A.2	K.CC.A.1	1	3												
K.CC.A.2	K.CC.A.1	1	4												
K.OA.A.2	K.OA.A.1	1	5												
K.OA.A.2	K.OA.A.1	2	6												
K.G.B.4	K.G.A.2	2	7												
K.G.B.4	K.G.A.2	1	8												
K.CC.B.4.B	K.CC.A.2	1	9												
	K.OA.A.2	2	10												

1 Choose all the groups of the number.

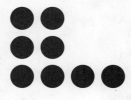 

     ○   ○   ○

2 Does the set show 9? Choose Yes or No.

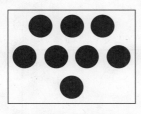   ○ Yes   ○ No

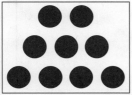   ○ Yes   ○ No

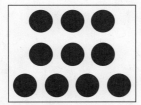   ○ Yes   ○ No

Connect the dots in order.

3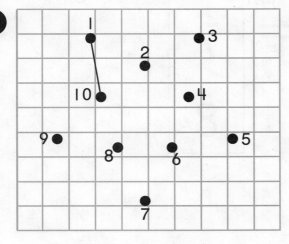

4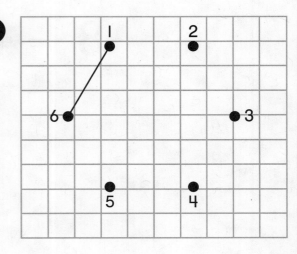

5 Ring the 5-group. Count the total. Write the number.

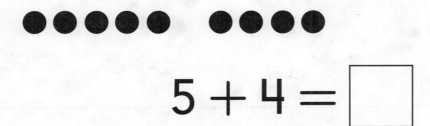

$$5 + 4 = \boxed{}$$

6 There are 8 circles. Draw a set of circles that shows 8 − 1.

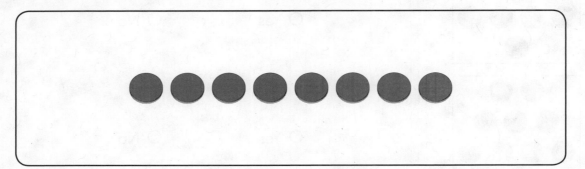

Ring the number that completes the number sentence.

$$8 - 1 = \begin{array}{|c|} \hline 6 \\ 7 \\ 8 \\ \hline \end{array}$$

7 Draw 3 triangles in the box. Write how many sides a triangle has.

A triangle has _____ sides.

8 Draw a line under the hexagons.

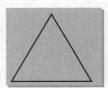   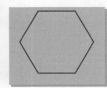

9 Look at the number tiles. Write the numbers 6 through 10 in order.

| 6 | 8 | 7 | 9 | 10 |

| 5 | | | | | |

---

10 Draw a picture that shows 7 + 1 squares.
Write how many squares.

Item Number	CCSS		DoK	Last Name, First Name
1	K.CC.B.5		1	
2	K.CC.B.5		1	
3	K.CC.A.1	K.CC.A.2	1	
4	K.CC.A.1	K.CC.A.2	1	
5	K.OA.A.1	K.OA.A.2	1	
6	K.G.A.2	K.G.B.4	1	
7	K.CC.A.2		1	
8	K.G.A.2	K.OA.A.1	2	
9	K.G.A.2		2	
10	K.OA.A.2	K.G.A.2	2	

Fill in the ◯ for the correct answer.

Which group shows the number?

❶

8

○

○

○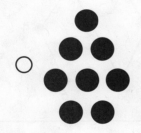

❷

9

○

○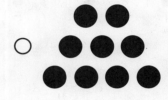

○

Which shows the dots connected in order?

3

○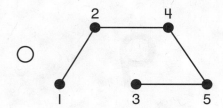

○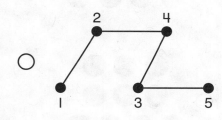

○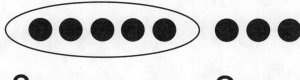

4

○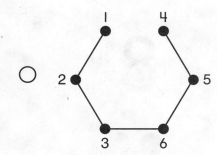

○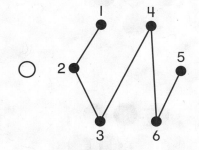

○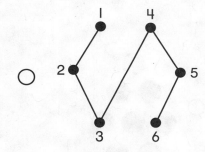

5 The 5-group is circled. Count the total. Which shows the number?

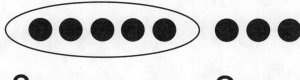

○ 8   ○ 9   ○ 10

6 Which shape is a hexagon?

  ○    ○    ○

7 Which number is missing from 5 to 10?

| 5 | 6 | 7 | 8 | | 10 |

○ 7   ○ 9   ○ 10

8 Draw a set of circles that shows 7 – 1.

9 Draw 2 triangles in the box. Write how many sides a triangle has.

A triangle has ☐ sides.

10 Draw a picture that shows 8 + 1 triangles.
Write how many triangles.

Name _____   Date _____

Marco's Animals

Count the total. Write the number.

1

_____
- - - - - - -
_____ cats

_____
- - - - - - -
_____ dogs

2

_____
- - - - - - -
_____

DIRECTIONS **1.** Marco puts all his toy cats in a line. He puts all his toy dogs in a circle. Look at the picture of Marco's toys. How many cats does Marco have? Write the number. How many dogs does Marco have? Write the number. **2.** Marco has toy mice, too. He wants to arrange a number of mice that is one greater than the number of dogs. Draw Marco's toy mice. Write the number of mice you drew.

3

4

_____

- - - - - - -

_____

DIRECTIONS **3.** Marco has a fish tank with red and blue fish. There are 5 red fish. The number of blue fish is 1 less than the number of red fish. Draw Marco's fish. **4.** Write the number of fish there are in the tank in all.

Represent, Count, and Write Numbers 6 to 9

Marco's Animals

COMMON CORE STANDARDS

K.CC.A.3   Write numbers from 0 to 20. Represent a number of objects within a written numeral 0–20 (with 0 representing a count of no objects).

K.CC.B.5   Count to answer "how many?" questions about as many as 20 things arranged in a line, a rectangular array, or a circle, or as many as 10 things in a scattered configuration; given a number from 1 to 20, count out that many objects.

K.CC.C.6   Identify whether the number of objects in one group is greater than, less than, or equal to the number of objects in another group, e.g., by using matching and counting strategies.

PURPOSE

To assess the ability to count objects in a line and in a circle; count out a quantity of objects to match a given number; compare quantities of objects; and write numerals and number words to represent quantities

ESTIMATED TIME

25–30 minutes

GROUPING

Individuals

MATERIALS

- Copy of the task for each student, paper, pencil
- Crayons (red and blue)

PREPARATION HINTS

- Review counting sets of objects with children before assigning the task.
- Review writing numerals and number words to 9 with children before assigning the task.
- Review vocabulary, including *six*, *seven*, *eight*, *nine*, *greater*, *less*.

IMPLEMENTATION NOTES

- Read the task aloud to children and make sure that all children have a clear understanding of the task.
- Children may use manipulatives to complete the task.
- Allow children as much paper as they need to complete the task.
- Allow as much time as children need to complete the task.
- Children must complete the task individually, without collaboration.
- Collect all work when the task is complete.

TASK SUMMARY

Children count objects in a line and in a circle and write numerals to represent the quantities. They count out a number of objects that is one greater or one less than a given number and then write the numeral and number word.

REPRESENTATION

In this task teachers can...

- Help children make connections between auditory and visual information.
- Guide children to notice critical details contained in pictures on the page.

ACTION and EXPRESSION

In this task teachers can...

- Help children approach the task methodically by marking or touching the page to show their progress.
- Help children monitor progress by keeping track of goals.

ENGAGEMENT

In this task teachers can...

- Provide options for self-regulation by encouraging children to go back and check that they completed every part of the task.

EXPECTED STUDENT OUTCOMES

- Reflect engagement in a productive struggle
- Count and model sets of objects to 9
- Write numerals and number words to represent quantities of objects to 9

SCORING

Use the associated rubric to evaluate each child's work.

MARCO'S ANIMALS

Problem # The student:	Points
1. • counts the number of cats accurately and writes the corresponding number	1
• counts the number of dogs accurately and writes the corresponding number	1
2. • draws 8 mice	1
• writes the corresponding number	1
3. • draws 5 red fish	1
• draws 4 blue fish	1
4. • counts the number of fish in the fish tank	1
• writes the corresponding number: 9.	1
TOTAL POINTS:	8

**Point Score and equivalent Performance Level
(see rubrics below):**

   7–8 points = Level 3

   5–6 points = Level 2

   3–4 points = Level 1

   1–2 points = Level 0

MARCO'S ANIMALS

A level 3 response	• Indicates that the child has made sense of the task and persevered • Demonstrates an understanding of counting and comparing sets of objects in various configurations • Indicates an understanding of the relationship between numerals, number words, and the quantities they represent • Shows the ability to accurately apply understanding of numbers to generate a specified quantity of objects
A level 2 response	• Indicates that the child has made sense of the task and persevered • Demonstrates an understanding of counting and comparing sets of objects in various configurations • Indicates an understanding of the relationship between numerals, number words, and the quantities they represent • Shows the ability to accurately apply understanding of numbers to generate a specified quantity of objects • Addresses most or all aspects of the task, but there may be errors of omission
A level 1 response	• Shows that the child has made sense of at least some elements of the task • Shows evidence of understanding of how to count and compare sets of objects in various configurations • Demonstrates some understanding of the relationship between numerals, number words, and quantities • May not show the ability to accurately count, write, or represent some numbers
A level 0 response	• Shows little evidence that the child has made sense of the problems of the task • Reflects a lack of understanding of how to count, model, compare, and represent numbers • Shows little evidence of addressing the elements of the task

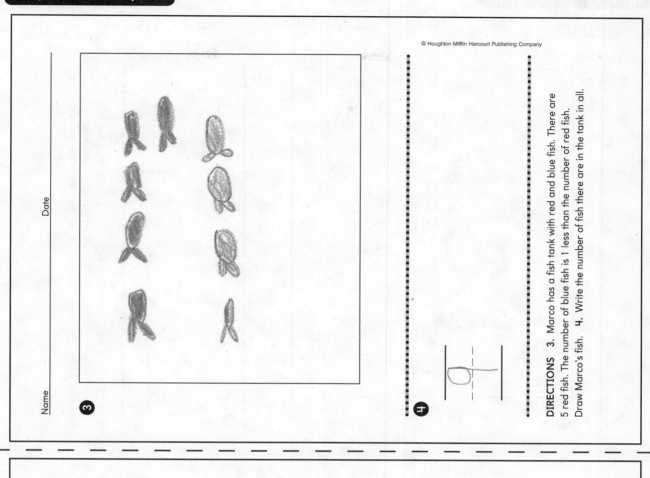

Name _____ Date _____

③

© Houghton Mifflin Harcourt Publishing Company

④

DIRECTIONS **3.** Marco has a fish tank with red and blue fish. There are 5 red fish. The number of blue fish is 1 less than the number of red fish. Draw Marco's fish. **4.** Write the number of fish there are in the tank in all.

Name _____ Date _____

Unit 2
Performance
Assessment

Marco's Animals

Count the total. Write the number.

① ___ cats

___ dogs

②

___

DIRECTIONS **1.** Marco puts all his toy cats in a line. He puts all his toy dogs in a circle. Look at the picture of Marco's toys. How many cats does Marco have? Write the number. How many dogs does Marco have? Write the number. **2.** Marco has toy mice, too. He wants to arrange a number of mice that is one greater than the number of dogs. Draw Marco's toy mice. Write the number of mice you drew.

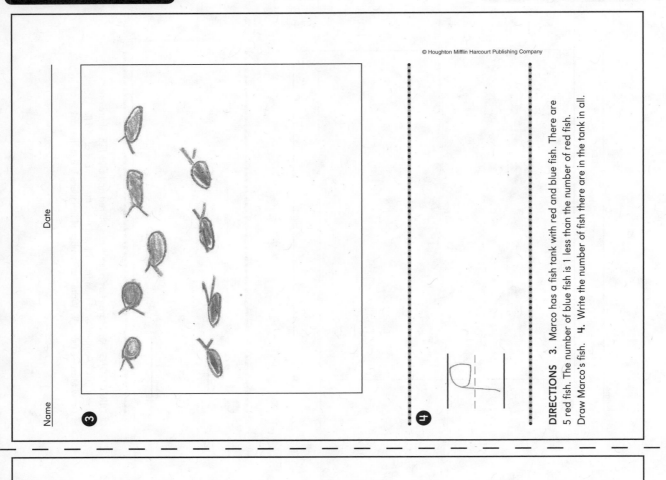

Name _____ Date _____

③

④

DIRECTIONS **3.** Marco has a fish tank with red and blue fish. There are 5 red fish. The number of blue fish is 1 less than the number of red fish. Draw Marco's fish. **4.** Write the number of fish there are in the tank in all.

Name _____ Date _____

Marco's Animals

Count the total. Write the number.

① _____ cats

_____ dogs

②

DIRECTIONS **1.** Marco puts all his toy cats in a line. He puts all his toy dogs in a circle. Look at the picture of Marco's toys. How many cats does Marco have? Write the number. How many dogs does Marco have? Write the number. **2.** Marco has toy mice, too. He wants to arrange a number of mice that is one greater than the number of dogs. Draw Marco's toy mice. Write the number of mice you drew.

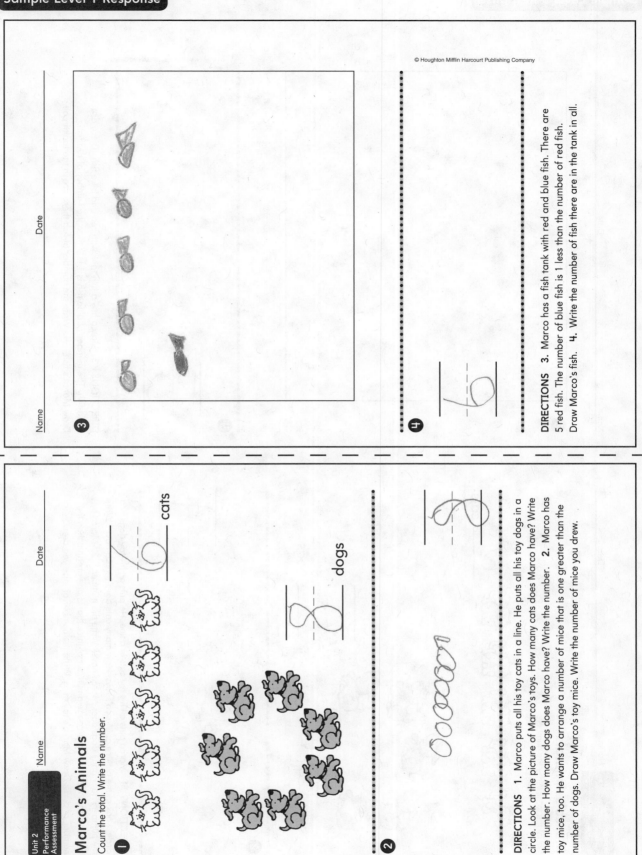

Name _____ Date _____

③

④ | 5

DIRECTIONS 3. Marco has a fish tank with red and blue fish. There are 5 red fish. The number of blue fish is 1 less than the number of red fish. Draw Marco's fish. **4.** Write the number of fish there are in the tank in all.

Name _____ Date _____

Unit 2
Performance
Assessment

Marco's Animals

① Count the total. Write the number.

_7_ cats

_8_ dogs

② | 8

0000000

DIRECTIONS 1. Marco puts all his toy cats in a line. He puts all his toy dogs in a circle. Look at the picture of Marco's toys. How many cats does Marco have? Write the number. How many dogs does Marco have? Write the number. **2.** Marco has toy mice, too. He wants to arrange a number of mice that is one greater than the number of dogs. Draw Marco's toy mice. Write the number of mice you drew.

Name _____ Date _____

③

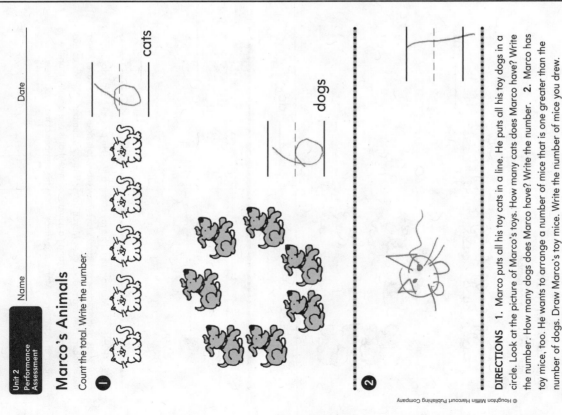

④

DIRECTIONS 3. Marco has a fish tank with red and blue fish. There are 5 red fish. The number of blue fish is 1 less than the number of red fish. Draw Marco's fish. **4.** Write the number of fish there are in the tank in all.

Name _____ Date _____

Marco's Animals

Count the total. Write the number.

①

_____ cats

_____ dogs

②

DIRECTIONS 1. Marco puts all his toy cats in a line. He puts all his toy dogs in a circle. Look at the picture of Marco's toys. How many cats does Marco have? Write the number. How many dogs does Marco have? Write the number. **2.** Marco has toy mice, too. He wants to arrange a number of mice that is one greater than the number of dogs. Draw Marco's toy mice. Write the number of mice you drew.

© Houghton Mifflin Harcourt Publishing Company

Item Number	DoK	CCSS	CCSS
1	1	K.OA.A.3	
2	1	K.OA.A.3	
3	1	K.NBT.A.1	
4	1	K.OA.A.1	
5	2	K.CC.A.3	K.CC.C.6
6	2	K.OA.A.3	K.CC.B.4.A
7	1	K.OA.A.5	
8	1	K.OA.A.5	
9	2	K.G.B.4	K.MD.B.3
10	2	K.G.A.2	K.MD.B.3
11	2	K.G.A.2	K.MD.B.3
12	2	K.G.A.2	K.MD.B.3
13	2	K.G.B.6	K.G.A.2
14	1	K.G.A.1	
15	2	K.OA.A.2	

Last Name, First Name

Write the partners.

1

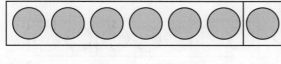

7

[ ] + [ ]

2

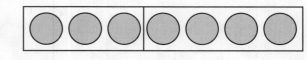

7

[ ] + [ ]

3 Ring a group of 10. Count all of the baseballs.
Write how many in all.

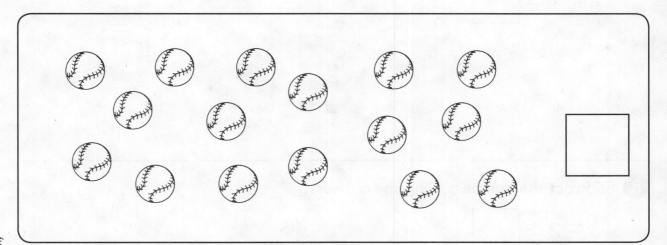

4 Ring the number. Draw it using the 5-group.

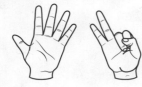

| 6 |
| 7 |
| 8 |

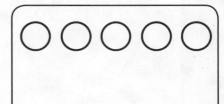

5 Write each number. Ring = or ≠.

6 Choose all the partners that are equal to 6.

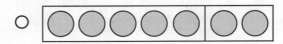

○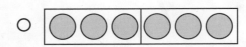

○

○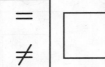

---

7 Add the numbers. Ring the answer.

2 + 1 = ☐

| 1 | 2 | 3 |

---

8 Subtract the numbers. Ring the answer.

3 − 2 = ☐

| 1 | 2 | 3 |

Name _____   Date _____

Use the pictures below to complete Exercises 9–12.

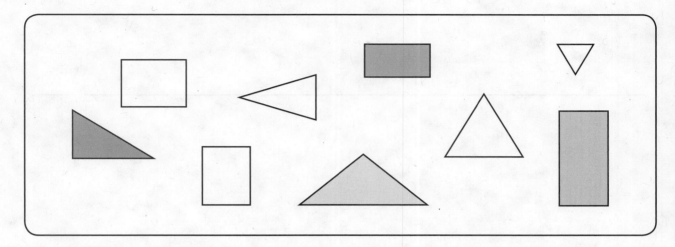

9 Ring all of the three-sided shapes.

_____

10 How many triangles are there?

    ○ **3**   ○ **4**   ○ **5**

_____

11 How many rectangles are there?

    ○ **3**   ○ **4**   ○ **5**

_____

12 Are there more triangles or rectangles? Ring the shape with more.

   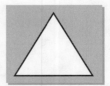

13 Two triangles are joined. Draw a shape they could make.

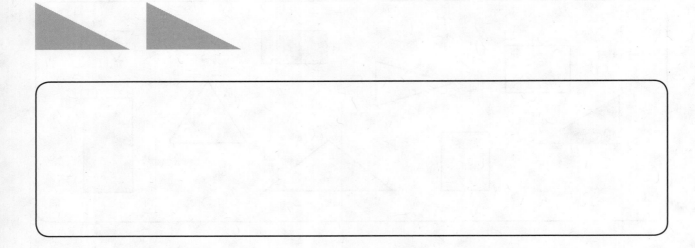

14 Draw a square. Draw a circle next to it.

15 Draw to show the story problem. Write the answer.

Rashid has 5 crackers. Juan has 4 crackers.

How many crackers do they have in all?

Item Number	DoK	CCSS	CCSS	Last Name, First Name
1	1	K.OA.3		
2	1	K.OA.3		
3	1	K.NBT.A.1		
4	2	K.G.B.6	K.G.A.2	
5	1	K.OA.5		
6	1	K.OA.5		
7	1	K.OA.5		
8	1	K.OA.5		
9	1	K.OA.5		
10	1	K.OA.5		
11	2	K.G.A.2	K.MD.B.3	
12	2	K.G.A.2	K.MD.B.3	
13	2	K.G.A.2	K.MD.B.3	
14	2	K.NBT.A.1		
15	1	K.G.A.1		
16	1	K.OA.1	K.OA.2	
17	1	K.OA.3	K.CC.B.5	
18	1	K.OA.1		
19	1	K.CC.C.6	K.CC.B.4.B	

Fill in the ◯ for the correct answer.

Which partners does the drawing show?

1

6

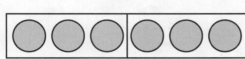

○ 3 + 5

○ 2 + 4

○ 3 + 3

2

7

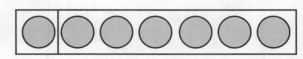

○ 2 + 5

○ 1 + 6

○ 5 + 1

3 Use the group of 10. How many in all?

12   13   14
○   ○   ○

Name _____ **Date** _____

4 Two triangles are joined. Which new shape could they make?

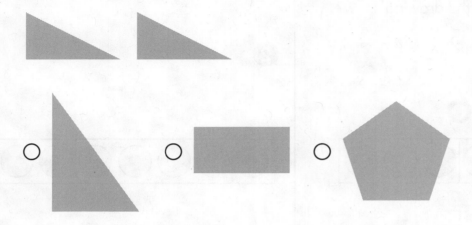

○   ○ ▭ ○ ⬠

Add.

5 3 + 2 =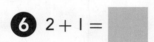

○ 5

○ 4

○ 1

6 2 + 1 =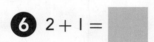

○ 1

○ 2

○ 3

7 3 + 1 =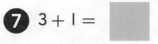

○ 4

○ 2

○ 1

Name _____ Date _____

Subtract.

8 $4 - 4 = $ ⬜

○ 4
○ 1
○ 0

9 $4 - 2 = $ ⬜

○ 2
○ 3
○ 4

10 $3 - 2 = $ ⬜

○ 0
○ 1
○ 5

Use the pictures below to complete Exercises 11–13.

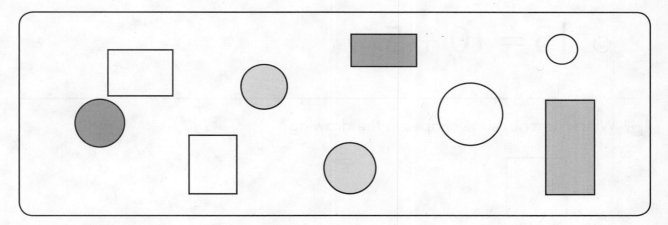

11 How many circles are there?

○ 3   ○ 4   ○ 5

12 How many rectangles are there?

○ 3   ○ 4   ○ 5

13 Which shape has more?

○ rectangle   ○ circles

14 Which equation does the drawing show?

○ $17 = 10 + 7$

○ $16 = 10 + 6$

○ $15 = 10 + 5$

---

15 Which describes the shapes in the drawing?

○ A circle is below a square.

○ A triangle is above a circle.

○ A circle is above a square.

16 Pete found 5 shells.
Lori found 3 shells.
How many shells did they
find in all?

○ 2

○ 8

○ 9

17 Write the partners.

8

□ + □

---

18 Ring the number. Draw it using the 5-group.

8

9

10

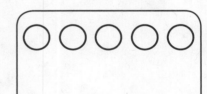

---

19 Write each number. Ring = or ≠.

□   = / ≠   □

Sharing Stickers

1

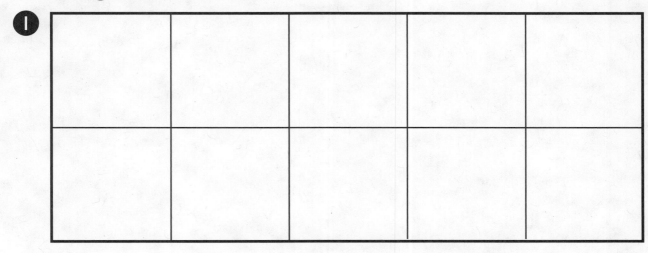

2

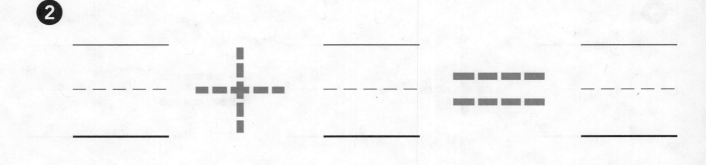

3

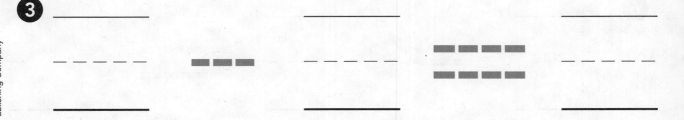

DIRECTIONS 1. Ana has 6 star stickers. Someone gives her 4 heart stickers. Put counters in the ten frame to show how many stickers Ana has in all. Draw the counters. **2.** Write the number sentence that tells about the stickers. **3.** Ana gives the 4 heart stickers to Paul. Cross out on your drawing to show the stickers Ana gives away. Write the number sentence that tells how many stickers Ana has left.

4

_____

5

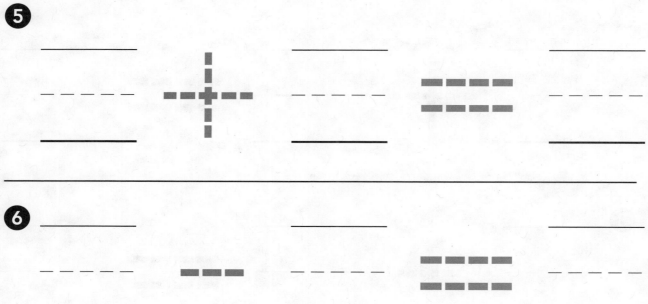

_____

6

_____

DIRECTIONS 4. Dylan has 9 stickers. Some are red and some are blue. Use cubes to show Dylan's stickers. Draw the cubes. **5.** Write a number sentence that tells about Dylan's stickers. **6.** What if Dylan gives his blue stickers away? Cross out on your drawing to show the stickers Dylan gives away. Write the number sentence that tells how many stickers Dylan has left.

Subtraction

Sharing Stickers

COMMON CORE STANDARDS

K.OA.A.1   Represent addition and subtraction with objects, fingers, mental images, drawings, sounds (e.g., claps), acting out situations, verbal explanations, expressions, or equations.

K.OA.A.2   Solve addition and subtraction word problems, and add and subtract within 10, e.g., by using objects or drawings to represent the problem.

K.OA.A.5   Fluently add and subtract within 5.

PURPOSE

To assess the ability to solve addition and subtraction word problems within 10 using models, drawings, and equations

ESTIMATED TIME

25–30 minutes

GROUPING

Individuals

MATERIALS

- Copy of the task for each student, paper, pencil
- Two-color counters
- Connecting cubes
- Crayons or colored pencils

PREPARATION HINTS

- Review modeling addition as "putting together" and subtraction as "taking from" with children before assigning the task.
- Review writing addition and subtraction sentences with children before assigning the task.
- Review vocabulary, including *number sentence.*

IMPLEMENTATION NOTES

- Read the task aloud to children and make sure that all children have a clear understanding of the task.
- Children may use manipulatives to complete the task.
- Allow children as much paper as they need to complete the task.
- Allow as much time as children need to complete the task.
- Children must complete the task individually, without collaboration.
- Collect all work when the task is complete.

TASK SUMMARY

Children make models and draw pictures to solve addition and subtraction word problems within 10. They record the addition and subtraction using number sentences.

REPRESENTATION

In this task teachers can...

- Provide options for language, mathematical expressions, and symbols by reviewing vocabulary and symbols in the context of children's prior knowledge.
- Provide options for comprehension by asking children to visualize scenarios in their minds.

ACTION and EXPRESSION

In this task teachers can...

- Provide options for physical action by offering manipulatives to children while completing the task.

ENGAGEMENT

In this task teachers can...

- Recruit interest by emphasizing the uniqueness of children's interpretations and engaging with children's stories.

EXPECTED STUDENT OUTCOMES

- Reflect engagement in a productive struggle
- Model and use equations to solve addition and subtraction within 10

SCORING

Use the associated rubric to evaluate each child's work.

SHARING STICKERS

Problem #		Points
The student:		
1.	• counts how many stickers Ana has in all: 10 stickers	1
	• uses counters and drawings to model	1
2.	• chooses the right addends	1
	• completes the number sentence accurately	1
3.	• completes the number sentence accurately: $10 - 4 = 6$	1
	• models the story problem	1
4.	• chooses the correct partners for 9	1
	• uses drawings or manipulatives to model the story problem	1
5.	• chooses the right addends	1
	• completes the number sentence accurately	1
6.	• completes the number sentence accurately	1
	• models the story problem to show reasoning.	1
	TOTAL POINTS:	12

Point Score and equivalent Performance Level
(see rubrics below):

    10–12 points = Level 3

    7–9 points = Level 2

    4–6 points = Level 1

    1–3 points = Level 0

SHARING STICKERS

A level 3 response	• Indicates that the child has made sense of the task and persevered • Demonstrates an understanding of addition as "putting together" groups and subtraction as "taking from" a group • Indicates an understanding of the parts of addition and subtraction sentences • Shows an ability to model and solve addition and subtraction word problems within 10
A level 2 response	• Indicates that the child has made sense of the task and persevered • Demonstrates an understanding of addition as "putting together" groups and subtraction as "taking from" a group • Indicates an understanding of the parts of addition and subtraction sentences • Shows an ability to model and solve addition and subtraction word problems within 10 • Addresses most or all aspects of the task, but there may be errors of omission
A level 1 response	• Shows that the child has made sense of at least some elements of the task • Shows evidence of understanding of situations involving "putting together" groups and "taking from" a group • Indicates some understanding of the parts of addition and subtraction sentences • May not present accurate representations or solutions
A level 0 response	• Shows little evidence that the child has made sense of the problems of the task • Reflects a lack of understanding of addition as "putting together" groups and subtraction as "taking from" a group • Reflects a lack of understanding of the parts of addition and subtraction sentences • Shows little evidence of addressing the elements of the task

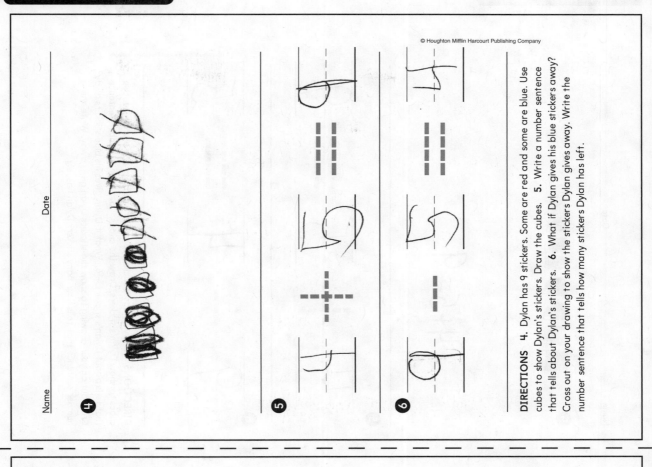

Name _____ Date _____

④

⑤

4 ⊕ 5 = 9

⑥

9 ⊟ 5 = 4

© Houghton Mifflin Harcourt Publishing Company

DIRECTIONS 4. Dylan has 9 stickers. Some are red and some are blue. Use cubes to show Dylan's stickers. Draw the cubes. **5.** Write a number sentence that tells about Dylan's stickers. **6.** What if Dylan gives his blue stickers away? Cross out on your drawing to show the stickers Dylan gives away. Write the number sentence that tells how many stickers Dylan has left.

© Houghton Mifflin Harcourt Publishing Company

Sharing Stickers

Name _____ Date _____

①

②

6 ⊕ 4 = 10

③

10 ⊟ 4 = 6

© Houghton Mifflin Harcourt Publishing Company

DIRECTIONS 1. Ana has 6 star stickers. Someone gives her 4 heart stickers. Put counters in the ten frame to show how many stickers Ana has in all. Draw the counters. **2.** Write the number sentence that tells about the stickers. **3.** Ana gives the 4 heart stickers to Paul. Cross out on your drawing to show the stickers Ana gives away. Write the number sentence that tells how many stickers Ana has left.

Name _____ Date _____

4.

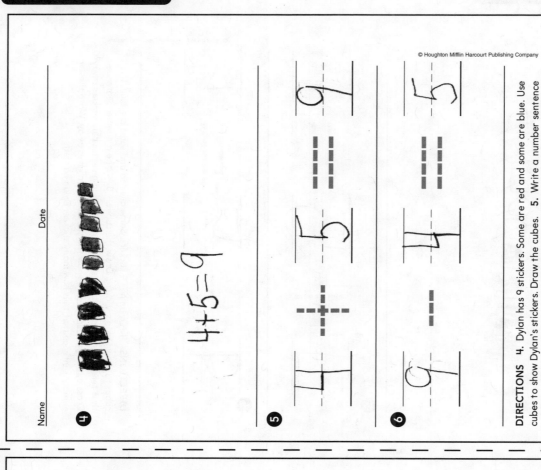

$4 + 5 = 9$

5. $4 + 5 = 9$

6. $9 - 4 = 5$

DIRECTIONS **4.** Dylan has 9 stickers. Some are red and some are blue. Use cubes to show Dylan's stickers. Draw the cubes. **5.** Write a number sentence that tells about Dylan's stickers. **6.** What if Dylan gives his blue stickers away? Cross out on your drawing to show the stickers Dylan gives away. Write the number sentence that tells how many stickers Dylan has left.

Name _____ Date _____

Sharing Stickers

1.

2. $6 + 4 = 10$

3. $10 - 4 = 6$

DIRECTIONS **1.** Ana has 6 star stickers. Someone gives her 4 heart stickers. Put counters in the ten frame to show how many stickers Ana has in all. Draw the counters. **2.** Write the number sentence that tells about the stickers. **3.** Ana gives the 4 heart stickers to Paul. Cross out on your drawing to show the stickers Ana gives away. Write the number sentence that tells how many stickers Ana has left.

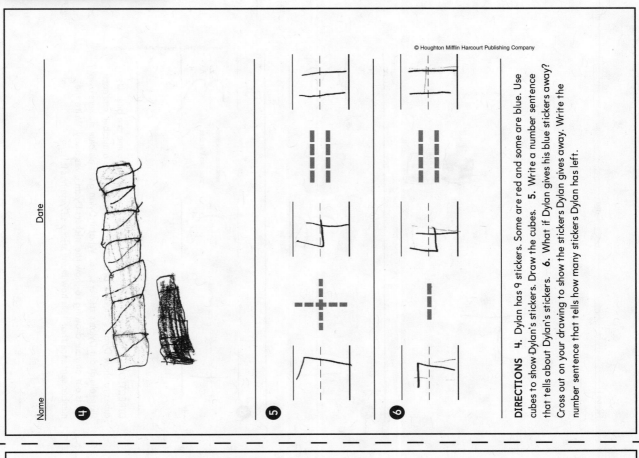

Name _____ Date _____

DIRECTIONS 4. Dylan has 9 stickers. Some are red and some are blue. Use cubes to show Dylan's stickers. Draw the cubes. **5.** Write a number sentence that tells about Dylan's stickers. **6.** What if Dylan gives his blue stickers away? Cross out on your drawing to show the stickers Dylan gives away. Write the number sentence that tells how many stickers Dylan has left.

Name _____ Date _____

Unit 3
Performance
Assessment

Sharing Stickers

DIRECTIONS 1. Ana has 6 star stickers. Someone gives her 4 heart stickers. Put counters in the ten frame to show how many stickers Ana has in all. Draw the counters. **2.** Write the number sentence that tells about the stickers. **3.** Ana gives the 4 heart stickers to Paul. Cross out on your drawing to show the stickers Ana gives away. Write the number sentence that tells how many stickers Ana has left.

Name _____ Date _____

Unit 3
Performance
Assessment

Sharing Stickers

1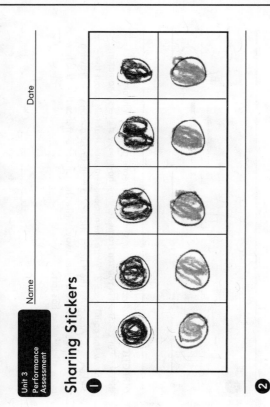

2 1 + 4 = 5 ☆

3 5 - 2 = 3

DIRECTIONS 1. Ana has 6 star stickers. Someone gives her 4 heart stickers. Put counters in the ten frame to show how many stickers Ana has in all. Draw the counters. **2.** Write the number sentence that tells about the stickers. **3.** Ana gives the 4 heart stickers to Paul. Cross out on your drawing to show the stickers Ana gives away. Write the number sentence that tells how many stickers Ana has left.

Name _____ Date _____

4 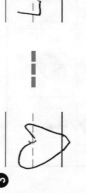 5

5 1 + 2 = 3

6 1 - 2 = 3

DIRECTIONS 4. Dylan has 9 stickers. Some are red and some are blue. Use cubes to show Dylan's stickers. Draw the cubes. **5.** Write a number sentence that tells about Dylan's stickers. **6.** What if Dylan gives his blue stickers away? Cross out on your drawing to show the stickers Dylan gives away. Write the number sentence that tells how many stickers Dylan has left.

© Houghton Mifflin Harcourt Publishing Company

Item Number	CCSS	DoK	Last Name, First Name
1	K.CC.A.1	1	
2	K.CC.A.2	1	
3	K.CC.A.3	2	
4	K.CC.B.4.A	1	
5	K.CC.B.4.B	2	
6	K.CC.B.4.C	2	
7	K.CC.B.5	1	
8	K.CC.C.6	2	
9	K.CC.C.7	2	
10	K.CC.C.7	2	
11	K.OA.A.3	1	
12	K.OA.A.5	1	
13	K.OA.A.2	2	
14	K.OA.A.3	2	
15	K.OA.A.4	1	
16	K.OA.A.5	1	
17	K.OA.A.5	1	
18	K.NBT.A.1	2	

CCSS	DoK	Item Number	Last Name, First Name														
K.NBT.A.1	1	19															
K.NBT.A.1	1	20															
K.MD.A.1	2	21															
K.MD.A.2	2	22															
K.MD.B.3	2	23															
K.G.A.1	2	24															
K.G.A.2	1	25															
K.G.A.3	1	26															
K.G.A.3	1	27															
K.G.B.4	1	28															
K.G.B.4	1	29															
K.G.B.6	2	30															

Counting and Cardinality

1 Write the missing numbers from 1 to 15.

1													15

2 Circle the numbers that are in counting order.

6 7 8 9

6 8 9 10

5 7 9 10

3 How many trucks? Write the number.

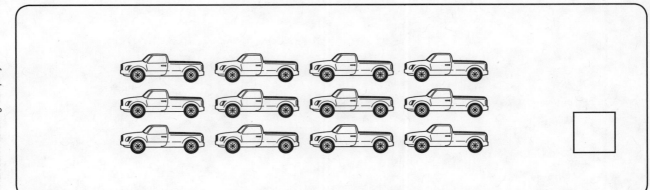

4 Circle the numbers that are in order when counting this group.

1, 2, 3, 4, 5

1, 3, 4, 5, 6

1, 2, 3, 5, 6

---

5 Circle the number you say last when counting this group.

7   8   9

6 Circle the number that comes next.

○○○
○○○
6

○○○○
○○○
7

○○○○○
○○○○○
10

○○○
○○○
○○○
9

○○○○
○○○○
8

---

7 Circle the group of 9 birds.

8 Circle the group that has less.

7

4

Compare the numbers.
Write G for **Greater than** or L for **Less than.**

9

| 2 | _____ | 6 |

10

| 9 | _____ | 5 |

Operations and Algebraic Thinking

11 Write the partners.

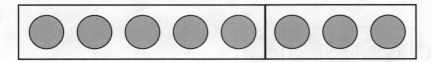

$8 = \boxed{} + \boxed{}$

---

12 Subtract the numbers.

$3 - 2 = \boxed{}$

---

13 Ben has 5 keys. Then he gives 2 keys away.
How many keys does Ben have left? Write the equation.

Equation: _____ − _____ = _____

14 Write the partners.

5

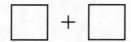

☐ + ☐

---

15 Write the partners.

10 = ☐ + ☐

---

16 Add the numbers.

1 + 2 = ☐

17 Subtract the numbers.

4 − 1 = ☐

Number and Operations in Base Ten

18 Circle a group of 10. Write how many in all.

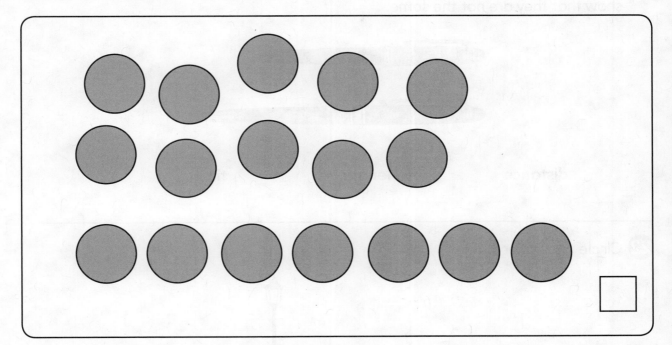

Write the total.

19

$$10 + 9 = \boxed{}$$

20

$$\boxed{} = 10 + 6$$

Measurement and Data

21 Circle the word that tells how the pens could be compared to show that they are not the same.

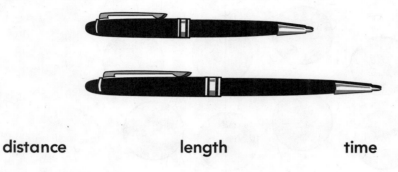

distance   length   time

---

22 Circle the taller light.

---

23 Count the squares and circles.
Circle the number that is more.

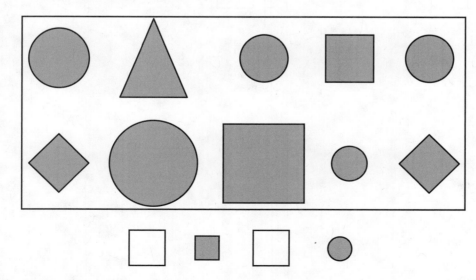

Geometry

24 Circle the cylinder that is beside the sphere.

---

25 Circle the square.

---

26 Circle the flat shape.

---

27 Circle the solid shape.

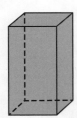 

28 Circle the shape that is like the first shape.

 |

29 Circle the shape that is shaped like the battery.

30 Cal stacks a cone and a sphere.

Circle the new shape that he makes.

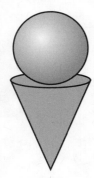 

CCSS	DoK	Item Number	Last Name, First Name												
K.CC.A.3	2	1													
K.OA.A.2	2	2													
K.CC.A.3	1	3													
K.OA.A.5	1	4													
K.OA.A.5	1	5													
K.CC.A.3	1	6													
K.CC.A.3	1	7													
K.NBT.A.1	1	8													
K.G.A.3	2	9													
K.G.A.2	2	10													
K.G.A.2	2	11													
K.G.A.2	2	12													
K.G.A.2	2	13													
K.G.A.1	2	14													
K.G.A.1	2	15													
K.NBT.A.1	2	16													

1 Count to find how many suns. Write the partners.

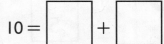

$10 = \boxed{} + \boxed{}$

2 Rick has 8 oranges. He eats 2 oranges.
Draw the oranges Rick has left.

3 Which partner of 10 does the picture show?

○ $10 = 4 + 6$

○ $10 = 7 + 3$

○ $10 = 9 + 1$

Add. Ring the answer.

 4 $1 + 4 =$
3
5

Subtract. Ring the answer.

 5 $3 - 0 =$
0
3

Count and write the number. Ring the number that is less.

6

7

8 Draw lines to match the equation to the drawing.

$10 + 4 = 14$ $10 + 3 = 13$ $10 + 1 = 11$

•   •   •

•   •   •

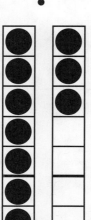      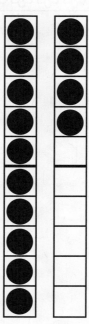

9 Choose all of the pictures that are solid shapes.

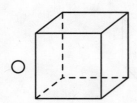 ○   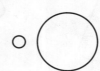 ○   ○ ◯   ○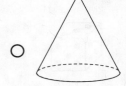

Use the pictures below to complete Exercises 10–13.

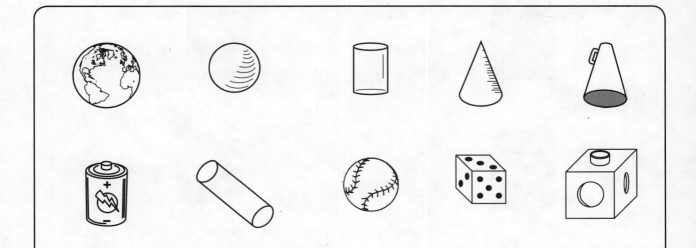

10 How many spheres are there? ☐

---

11 How many cylinders are there? ☐

---

12 How many cones are there? ☐

---

13 How many cubes are there? ☐

14 Ring the cube that is next to the cylinder.

---

15 Ring the tile that shows the cone above the cylinder.

---

16 Draw to show 17 as 10 ones and extra ones. Write the equation.

$10 + \boxed{} = \boxed{}$

CCSS	DoK	Item Number	Last Name, First Name													
K.NBT.A.1	—	1														
K.NBT.A.1	—	2														
K.OA.A.5	—	3														
K.OA.A.5	—	4														
K.OA.A.5	—	5														
K.OA.A.5	—	6														
K.OA.A.5	—	7														
K.OA.A.5	—	8														
K.OA.A.3	—	9														
K.OA.A.3	—	10														
K.NBT.A.1	—	11														
K.NBT.A.1	—	12														
K.G.A.2	2	13														
K.G.A.2	2	14														
K.G.A.1	2	15														
K.NBT.A.1	—	16														
K.OA.A.5	—	17														
K.OA.A.5	—	18														

CCSS	DoK	Item Number	Last Name, First Name												
K.OA.A.5	1	19													
K.OA.A.5	2	20													
K.OA.A.3	2	21													
K.OA.A.3	2	22													
K.CC.C.6	2	23													
K.CC.C.6	2	24													
K.OA.A.1	2	25													

Fill in the ◯ for the correct answer.

Which partners does the drawing show?

1 ✿✿✿✿✿✿ | ✿✿✿✿

- ◯ $10 = 6 + 4$
- ◯ $10 = 7 + 3$
- ◯ $10 = 8 + 2$

2 ✿✿✿✿✿✿✿ | ✿✿✿

- ◯ $10 = 5 + 5$
- ◯ $10 = 6 + 4$
- ◯ $10 = 7 + 3$

Add the numbers.

3 $5 + 0 =$ ▨

- ◯ 0
- ◯ 5
- ◯ 6

4 $1 + 4 =$ ▨

- ◯ 3
- ◯ 4
- ◯ 5

5 $3 + 1 =$ ▨

- ◯ 2
- ◯ 4
- ◯ 5

Subtract the numbers.

6 $3 - 0 =$ ▨

- ◯ 0
- ◯ 3
- ◯ 4

7 $4 - 2 =$ ▨

- ◯ 2
- ◯ 3
- ◯ 6

8 $5 - 1 =$ ▨

- ◯ 6
- ◯ 5
- ◯ 4

Which partners does the drawing show?

9

- ○ 7 = 5 + 2
- ○ 7 = 6 + 1
- ○ 7 = 7 + 0

10

- ○ 8 = 3 + 5
- ○ 8 = 2 + 7
- ○ 8 = 2 + 6

Complete the equation.

11 10 + 5 = ▨

- ○ 15
- ○ 14
- ○ 13

12 10 + 6 = ▨

- ○ 14
- ○ 15
- ○ 16

13 Which is a cylinder?

○   ○   ○

---

14 Which is a sphere?

○   ○   ○

---

15 Which is true about the cylinder?

○ It is above the cone.

○ It is behind the cone.

○ It is in front of the cone.

16 Which equation does the drawing show?

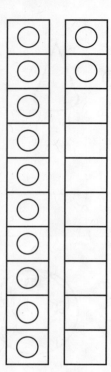

○ $10 + 3 = 13$

○ $10 + 2 = 12$

○ $10 + 1 = 11$

Add the numbers.

17 $1 + 3 =$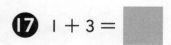

    ○ 4

    ○ 3

    ○ 1

18 $3 + 2 =$

    ○ 1

    ○ 4

    ○ 5

Subtract the numbers.

19 $4 - 1 =$ ⬜

- ○ 2
- ○ 3
- ○ 4

20 $5 - 2 =$ ⬜

- ○ 1
- ○ 2
- ○ 3

21 Which equation shows the partners?

- ○ $7 = 2 + 3$
- ○ $6 = 2 + 3$
- ○ $5 = 2 + 3$

22 Which drawing shows the partner equation?

$$10 = 6 + 4$$

- ○
- ○
- ○

23 Count and write the number. Ring the number that is less.

☐   ☐

---

24 Count and write the number. Ring the number that is more.

☐   ☐

---

25 Rose has 8 markers. She gives 3 away.

Draw the markers Rose has left.

Bees and Flowers

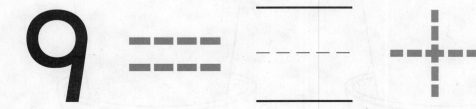

_____

2

_____

DIRECTIONS 1. Use counters to find partners for 9. Complete the addition sentence. 2. Now use the partners to draw or write an addition story about 9 bees.

3

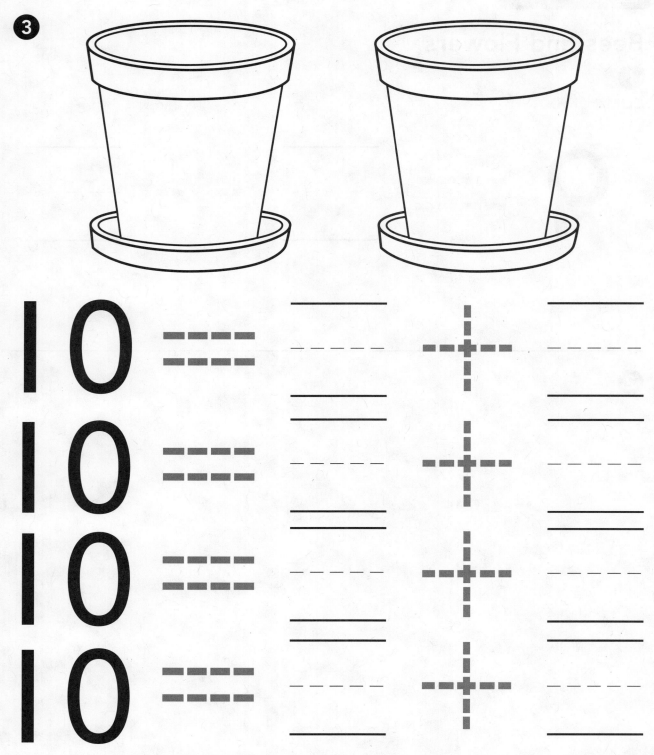

DIRECTIONS   3. Molly has 10 flowers. She would like to put the flowers into two pots. Use counters to show four different ways Molly could put the flowers in the pots. Write the addition sentence for each way. Then circle one of your addition sentences. Draw flowers in the pots to match your addition sentence.

Addition

Bees and Flowers

COMMON CORE STANDARDS

K.OA.A.1   Represent addition and subtraction with objects, fingers, mental images, drawings, sounds (e.g., claps), acting out situations, verbal explanations, expressions, or equations.

K.OA.A.2   Solve addition and subtraction word problems, and add and subtract within 10, e.g., by using objects or drawings to represent the problem.

K.OA.A.3   Decompose numbers less than or equal to 10 into pairs in more than one way, e.g., by using objects or drawings, and record each decomposition by a drawing or equation (e.g., $5 = 2 + 3$ and $5 = 4 + 1$).

PURPOSE

To assess the ability to model and write addition sentences for number pairs for a specified sum

ESTIMATED TIME

25–30 minutes

GROUPING

Individuals

MATERIALS

- Copy of the task for each student, paper, pencil
- Two-color counters

PREPARATION HINTS

- Review modeling number pairs for sums with children before assigning the task.
- Review writing addition sentences with children before assigning the task.
- Review vocabulary, including *nine*, *ten*, *pair*.

IMPLEMENTATION NOTES

- Read the task aloud to children and make sure that all children have a clear understanding of the task.
- Children may use manipulatives to complete the task.
- Allow children as much paper as they need to complete the task.
- Allow as much time as children need to complete the task.
- Children must complete the task individually, without collaboration.
- Collect all work when the task is complete.

TASK SUMMARY

Children model decomposing a number into pairs in more than one way. They write an addition sentence to record each decomposition. They draw or write a story to reflect the addition.

REPRESENTATION

In this task teachers can...

- Provide options for comprehension by having children use background knowledge to help them understand the task.
- Provide options for comprehension by using cues to draw attention to critical features.

ACTION and EXPRESSION

In this task teachers can...

- Provide options for expression and communication by allowing children to communicate their stories through multiple means.

ENGAGEMENT

In this task teachers can...

- Recruit interest by emphasizing uniqueness of children's interpretations.
- Recruit interest by engaging with children's stories.

EXPECTED STUDENT OUTCOMES

- Reflect engagement in a productive struggle
- Decompose a number into pairs in more than one way and write a number sentence to represent the addition
- Present an addition story with the sum of 9

SCORING

Use the associated rubric to evaluate each child's work.

BEES AND FLOWERS

Problem #	Points
The student:	
1. • chooses the correct partners for 9	1
2. • writes or draws an addition story to match the number sentence	2
3. • shows 4 sets of partners for 10	4
• models the number sentence accurately.	1
TOTAL POINTS:	8

**Point Score and equivalent Performance Level
(see rubrics below):**

7–8 points = Level 3

5–6 points = Level 2

3–4 points = Level 1

1–2 points = Level 0

BEES AND FLOWERS

A level 3 response	• Indicates that the child has made sense of the task and persevered
	• Demonstrates an understanding of decomposing a number into pairs in more than one way
	• Indicates an understanding of using a number sentence to record addition
	• Shows the ability to apply understanding of decomposing numbers in a math story
A level 2 response	• Indicates that the child has made sense of the task and persevered
	• Demonstrates an understanding of decomposing a number into pairs in more than one way
	• Indicates an understanding of using a number sentence to record addition
	• Shows the ability to apply understanding of decomposing numbers in a math story
	• Addresses most or all aspects of the task, but there may be errors of omission
A level 1 response	• Shows that the child has made sense of at least some elements of the task
	• Shows evidence of understanding of decomposing numbers into pairs
	• Indicates some understanding of using a number sentence to record addition
	• May not show the ability to accurately model decomposition or record addition
A level 0 response	• Shows little evidence that the child has made sense of the problems of the task
	• Reflects a lack of understanding of decomposing numbers and using number sentences to record addition
	• Shows little evidence of addressing the elements of the task

Name _____ Date _____

③

5 + 5 = 10

8 + 2 = 10

1 + 9 = 10

10 + 0 = 10

DIRECTIONS 3. Molly has 10 flowers. She would like to put the flowers into two pots. Use counters to show four different ways Molly could put the flowers in the pots. Write the addition sentence for each way. Then circle one of your addition sentences. Draw flowers in the pots to match your addition sentence.

Name _____ Date _____

Bees and Flowers

①

9 = 5 + 4

②

4 bees + 5 bees

DIRECTIONS 1. Use counters to find partners for 9. Complete the addition sentence. **2.** Now use the partners to draw or write an addition story about 9 bees.

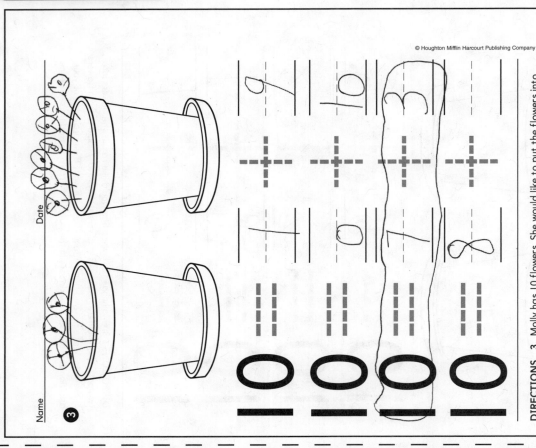

© Houghton Mifflin Harcourt Publishing Company

Name _____ Date _____

③

9 + 1 = 10

10 + 0 = 10

3 + 7 = 10

+ 8 = 10

DIRECTIONS 3. Molly has 10 flowers. She would like to put the flowers into two pots. Use counters to show four different ways Molly could put the flowers in the pots. Write the addition sentence for each way. Then circle one of your addition sentences. Draw flowers in the pots to match your addition sentence.

Name _____ Date _____

Bees and Flowers

① 9 = 1 + 9

②   9 cum.

no bees.

DIRECTIONS 1. Use counters to find partners for 9. Complete the addition sentence. **2.** Now use the partners to draw or write an addition story about 9 bees.

© Houghton Mifflin Harcourt Publishing Company

© Houghton Mifflin Harcourt Publishing Company

© Houghton Mifflin Harcourt Publishing Company

Name _____ Date _____

③

$$5 + 5 = 10$$

$$3 + 8 = 10$$

$$3 + 7 = 10$$

$$4 + 4 = 10$$

DIRECTIONS 3. Molly has 10 flowers. She would like to put the flowers into two pots. Use counters to show four different ways Molly could put the flowers in the pots. Write the addition sentence for each way. Then circle one of your addition sentences. Draw flowers in the pots to match your addition sentence.

© Houghton Mifflin Harcourt Publishing Company

Name _____ Date _____

Bees and Flowers

①

$$9 = 4 + 4$$

②

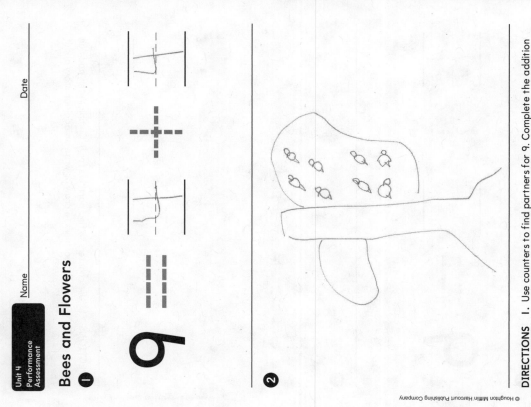

© Houghton Mifflin Harcourt Publishing Company

DIRECTIONS 1. Use counters to find partners for 9. Complete the addition sentence. **2.** Now use the partners to draw or write an addition story about 9 bees.

© Houghton Mifflin Harcourt Publishing Company

Name

Date

③

3 | + | 3 | = | 10

0 | + | 1 | = | 10

5 | + | 5 | = | 10

2 | + | 2 | = | 10

DIRECTIONS 3. Molly has 10 flowers. She would like to put the flowers into two pots. Use counters to show four different ways Molly could put the flowers in the pots. Write the addition sentence for each way. Then circle one of your addition sentences. Draw flowers in the pots to match your addition sentence.

Name

Date

Unit 4
Performance
Assessment

Bees and Flowers

① 9 = 4 + 9

②

DIRECTIONS 1. Use counters to find partners for 9. Complete the addition sentence. 2. Now use the partners to draw or write an addition story about 9 bees.

© Houghton Mifflin Harcourt Publishing Company

© Houghton Mifflin Harcourt Publishing Company

CCSS	CCSS	DoK	Item Number	Last Name, First Name												
	K.NBT.A.1	2	1													
	K.NBT.A.1	2	2													
	K.NBT.A.1	2	3													
	K.NBT.A.1	2	4													
	K.NBT.A.1	2	5													
K.OA.A.3	K.OA.A.1	—	6													
	K.CC.C.6	2	7													
K.CC.C.7	K.CC.C.6	2	8													
	K.OA.A.4	3	9													
	K.OA.A.4	3	10													
	K.OA.A.1	—	11													
	K.OA.A.1	—	12													
	K.OA.A.1	—	13													
	K.MD.A.2	—	14													
	K.MD.A.2	—	15													
	K.OA.A.2	2	16													

Write how many more than ten.
Draw circles to show each teen number.

1 15 = 10 + _____

---

2 16 = 10 + _____

---

3 17 = 10 + _____

Ring the ten ones.
Write the ten ones and more ones in each equation.

4

_____ + _____ = _____

5

_____ + _____ = _____

6 Draw a line to match the picture to the partner equation.

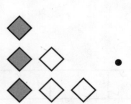

•

• $2 + 4 = 6$

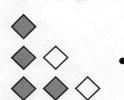

•

• $3 + 3 = 6$

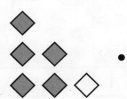

•

• $4 + 2 = 6$

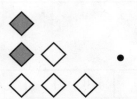

•

• $5 + 1 = 6$

7 Choose the symbol to show equal or not equal.

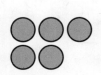
$=$
$\neq$

$=$
$\neq$

8 Write the numbers and compare them. Write **G** for **Greater** and **L** for **Less**. Cross out to make the groups equal.

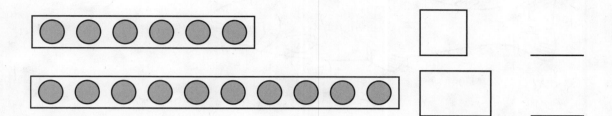

Draw Tiny Tumblers on the Math Mountain and write the equation partners. Complete the equation.

9 10

☐ + ☐ =

10 10

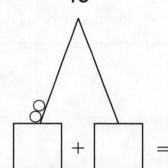

☐ + ☐ =

Use the numbers on the tiles to complete the equations.

| 6 | 7 | 8 | 9 | 10 |

11 8 + 1 = ☐   **12** 7 + 3 = ☐   **13** 6 + 2 = ☐

14 Choose the heavier object.

○

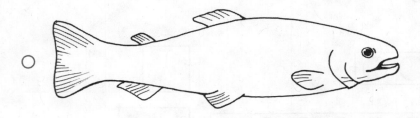

○

15 Draw a short flower and a tall flower. Ring the shorter one.

```



```

16 Draw to solve. Then write the equation.
There are 9 children playing at the park.
Then 2 of them go home.
How many children are still at the park?

Equation: _____ − _____ = _____

CCSS	DoK	Item Number	Last Name, First Name
K.NBT.A.1	1	1	
K.NBT.A.1	1	2	
K.NBT.A.1	1	3	
K.NBT.A.1	1	4	
K.OA.A.3	1	5	
K.OA.A.3	1	6	
K.OA.A.3	1	7	
K.OA.A.3	1	8	
K.OA.A.3	1	9	
K.OA.A.3	1	10	
K.OA.A.3	1	11	
K.OA.A.3	1	12	
K.OA.A.3	1	13	
K.OA.A.5	1	14	
K.OA.A.5	1	15	
K.OA.A.5	1	16	
K.OA.A.5	1	17	
K.OA.A.5	1	18	

CCSS	DoK	Item Number	Last Name, First Name												
K.CC.C.7	2	26													
K.NBT.A.1	2	25													
K.NBT.A.1	1	24													
K.NBT.A.1	1	23													
K.MD.A.2	2	22													
K.MD.A.2	1	21													
K.CC.C.6	1	20													
K.OA.A.5	1	19													

Fill in the ◯ for the correct answer.

What does the picture show?

1

18 = 10 + ▢

   ◯ **6**   ◯ **7**   ◯ **8**

---

2 The circles show the teen number.

How many more than ten?

19 = 10 + ▢

   ◯ **8**   ◯ **9**   ◯ **10**

Which equation shows the ten and the extra ones?

3

  ◯ 10 + 1 = 11

  ◯ 10 + 2 = 12

  ◯ 10 + 3 = 13

4

  ◯ 10 + 6 = 16

  ◯ 10 + 5 = 15

  ◯ 10 + 1 = 11

Which partners for 5 does the drawing show?

⑤ ▲△△△△

- ○ 2 + 3
- ○ 1 + 4
- ○ 3 + 2

⑥ ▲▲△△△

- ○ 2 + 3
- ○ 4 + 1
- ○ 1 + 4

Which partners for 5 does the drawing show?

⑦ ▲▲▲△△

- ○ 1 + 4
- ○ 4 + 1
- ○ 3 + 2

⑧ ▲▲▲▲△

- ○ 4 + 1
- ○ 3 + 2
- ○ 2 + 4

Which partners for 6 does the drawing show?

⑨

- ○ 1 + 5
- ○ 2 + 4
- ○ 3 + 3

⑩

- ○ 5 + 1
- ○ 3 + 3
- ○ 2 + 4

⑪

- ○ 2 + 4
- ○ 3 + 3
- ○ 4 + 2

Which partners for 6 does the drawing show?

12

- ○ 1 + 5
- ○ 3 + 3
- ○ 4 + 2

13

- ○ 3 + 3
- ○ 4 + 2
- ○ 5 + 1

Add.

14 3 + 2 =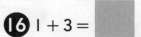

- ○ 4
- ○ 5
- ○ 6

15 2 + 1 =

- ○ 2
- ○ 3
- ○ 4

16 1 + 3 =

- ○ 2
- ○ 3
- ○ 4

Subtract.

17 6 − 3 =

- ○ 3
- ○ 4
- ○ 5

18 7 − 5 =

- ○ 1
- ○ 2
- ○ 3

19 5 − 4 =

- ○ 1
- ○ 2
- ○ 3

20 Which shows the correct way to compare the numbers?

○ 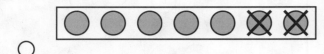    7   ___L___

    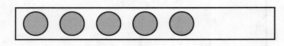   5   ___G___

○ 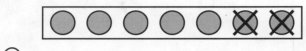   7   ___G___

    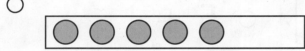   5   ___L___

○ 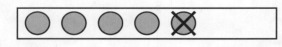   7   ___G___

    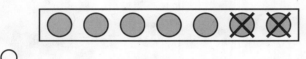   4   ___L___

21 Choose the object that is longer.

○

○

22 Choose the animal that is lighter.

○　　　　　　　　　　　　　　　○

---

23 There are 7 markers in the box.
There are 3 markers on the table.

Which equation shows how many markers in all?

○ $7 - 3 = 4$

○ $7 - 4 = 3$

○ $7 + 3 = 10$

---

24 What does the picture show?
Write the numbers on the lines.

____ ones and ____ ones

25 The circles show the teen number.
Write how many more than ten.

$18 = 10 + $ _____

---

26 Write the numbers and compare them.
Write **G** for **Greater** and **L** for **Less**.
Cross out to make the groups equal.

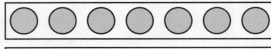

Buttons and Flowers

1

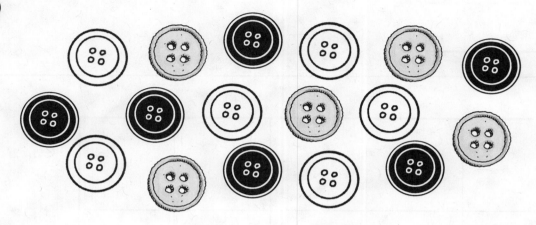

_____

- - - - - - - - - - - - - - - -

_____

2

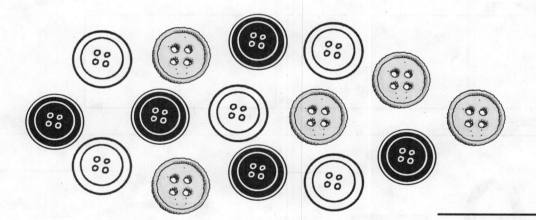

_____

- - - - - - - - - - - - - - - -

_____

DIRECTIONS   1–2. For each set, circle 10 buttons, count how many in all, and write the number.

Name _____   Date _____

3 _____

_____

4

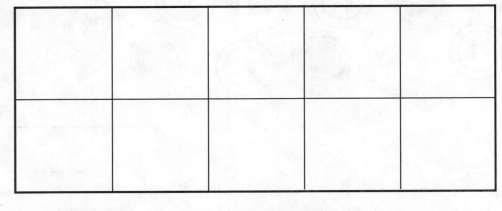

5 ## 10 + ____ = ____

DIRECTIONS **3.** Yoshi and Neela are picking flowers. They pick more than 10 flowers but no more than 19 flowers. Write a number that could be the number of flowers they pick. **4.** Place counters in the ten frames to show that number. Draw the counters. **5.** Complete the number sentence to show how to make that number.

Represent, Count, and Write 11 to 19

Buttons and Flowers

COMMON CORE STANDARDS

K.CC.A.3 Write numbers from 0 to 20. Represent a number of objects with a written numeral 0–20 (with 0 representing a count of no objects).

K.NBT.A.1 Compose and decompose numbers from 11 to 19 into ten ones and some further ones, e.g., by using objects or drawings, and record each composition or decomposition by a drawing or equation (e.g., 18 = 10 + 8); understand that these numbers are composed of ten ones and one, two, three, four, five, six, seven, eight, or nine ones.

PURPOSE

To assess the ability to write numbers from 11 to 19 and decompose them into ten ones and some further ones using models and equations

ESTIMATED TIME

25–30 minutes

GROUPING

Individuals

MATERIALS

- Copy of the task for each student, paper, pencil
- Crayons or colored pencils
- Two-color counters

PREPARATION HINTS

- Review numbers from 10 to 19 with children before assigning the task.
- Review decomposing numbers 11 to 19 into ten ones and some further ones with children before assigning the task.
- Review vocabulary, including *ten*, *more*.

IMPLEMENTATION NOTES

- Read the task aloud to children and make sure that all children have a clear understanding of the task.
- Children may use manipulatives to complete the task.
- Allow children as much paper as they need to complete the task.
- Allow as much time as children need to complete the task.
- Children must complete the task individually, without collaboration.
- Collect all work when the task is complete.

TASK SUMMARY

Children count and write numerals to represent quantities from 11 to 19. They decompose numbers from 11 to 19 into ten ones and some further ones using models and equations.

REPRESENTATION

In this task teachers can…

- Provide options for perception by offering alternative displays of visual information.
- Provide options for comprehension by making gestures to act out verbs contained in the directions.

ACTION and EXPRESSION

In this task teachers can…

- Provide options for physical action by allowing children to use counters to help them count.

ENGAGEMENT

In this task teachers can…

- Recruit interest by asking children to tell stories about their work.
- Encourage reflection by asking children to explain how they represented situations in story problems.

EXPECTED STUDENT OUTCOMES

- Complete the task within the time allowed
- Reflect engagement in a productive struggle
- Count, model, and write numbers from 11 to 19
- Decompose numbers from 11 to 19 into ten ones and some further ones

SCORING

Use the associated rubric to evaluate each child's work.

BUTTONS AND FLOWERS

Problem #	Points
The student:	
1. • accurately counts the number of buttons in all: 17 buttons	1
• uses ten groups to count accurately	1
2. • accurately counts the number of buttons in all: 15 buttons	1
• uses ten groups to count accurately	1
3. • chooses a number greater than 10 and less than 19	1
4. • models the number accurately	1
5. • chooses the correct addend	1
• completes the addition equation accurately.	1
TOTAL POINTS:	8

Point Score and equivalent Performance Level (see rubrics below):

7–8 points = Level 3

5–6 points = Level 2

3–4 points = Level 1

1–2 points = Level 0

BUTTONS AND FLOWERS

A level 3 response	• Indicates that the child has made sense of the task and persevered • Shows the ability to accurately count and write numerals to represent quantities from 11 to 19 • Shows the ability to compose quantities from 11 to 19 as ten ones and some further ones using models and addition sentences
A level 2 response	• Indicates that the child has made sense of the task and persevered • Shows the ability to accurately count and write numerals to represent quantities from 11 to 19 • Shows the ability to compose quantities from 11 to 19 as ten ones and some further ones using models and addition sentences • Addresses most or all aspects of the task, but there may be errors of omission
A level 1 response	• Shows that the child has made sense of at least some elements of the task • Shows evidence of understanding of how to count, model, and write numbers from 11 to 19 • Indicates some understanding of quantities from 11 to 19 as composed of ten ones and some further ones • May not accurately represent quantities or their decomposition
A level 0 response	• Shows little evidence that the child has made sense of the problems of the task • Reflects a lack of understanding of how to count, model, and write numbers from 11 to 19 • Reflects a lack of understanding of quantities from 11 to 19 as composed of ten ones and some further ones • Shows little evidence of addressing the elements of the task

Name _____ Date _____

③ 14

④

⑤ 10 + 4 = 14

DIRECTIONS 3. Yoshi and Neela are picking flowers. They pick more than 10 flowers but no more than 19 flowers. Write a number that could be the number of flowers they pick. **4.** Place counters in the ten frames to show that number. Draw the counters. **5.** Complete the number sentence to show how to make that number.

Name _____ Date _____

Unit 5 Performance Assessment

Buttons and Flowers

① 14

② 15

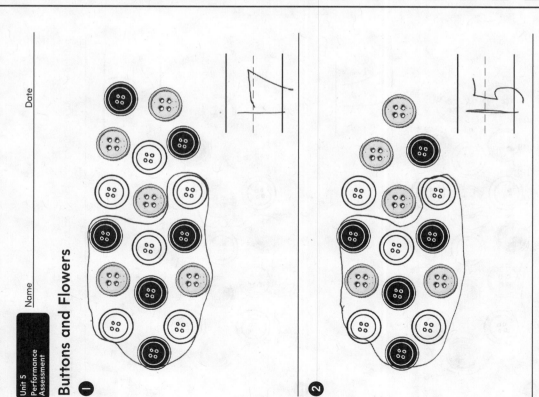

DIRECTIONS 1–2. For each set, circle 10 buttons, count how many in all, and write the number.

© Houghton Mifflin Harcourt Publishing Company

Name _____ Date _____

③ __17__

④

⑤ 10 + 7 = __

DIRECTIONS 3. Yoshi and Neela are picking flowers. They pick more than 10 flowers but no more than 19 flowers. Write a number that could be the number of flowers they pick. 4. Place counters in the ten frames to show that number. Draw the counters. 5. Complete the number sentence to show how to make that number.

Unit 5
Performance
Assessment

Buttons and Flowers

Name _____ Date _____

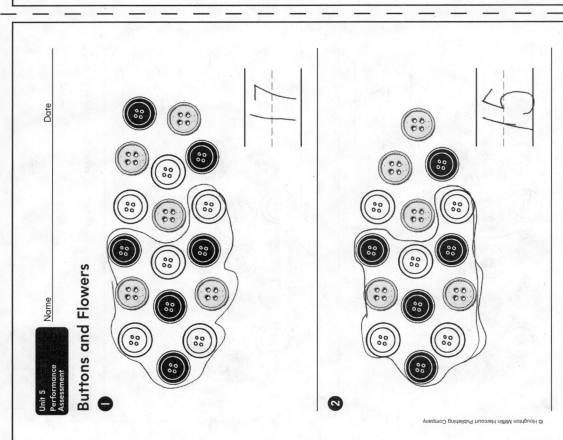

① __17__

② __15__

DIRECTIONS 1-2. For each set, circle 10 buttons, count how many in all, and write the number.

Name _____ Date _____

3 ⌇8⌇

4

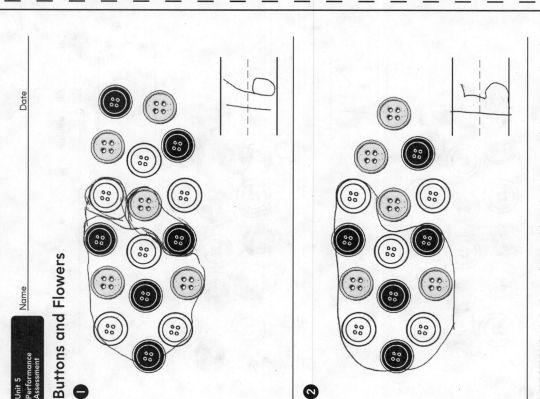

5 $10 + 8 = 18$

DIRECTIONS **3.** Yoshi and Neela are picking flowers. They pick more than 10 flowers but no more than 19 flowers. Write a number that could be the number of flowers they pick. **4.** Place counters in the ten frames to show that number. Draw the counters. **5.** Complete the number sentence to show how to make that number.

Name _____ Date _____

Buttons and Flowers

1 ⌇16⌇

2 ⌇15⌇

DIRECTIONS **1–2.** For each set, circle 10 buttons, count how many in all, and write the number.

Name _____ Date _____

③

④

⑤ 10 + ___ = ___

DIRECTIONS 3. Yoshi and Neela are picking flowers. They pick more than 10 flowers but no more than 19 flowers. Write a number that could be the number of flowers they pick. 4. Place counters in the ten frames to show that number. Draw the counters. 5. Complete the number sentence to show how to make that number.

Name _____ Date _____

Buttons and Flowers

①

②

DIRECTIONS 1–2. For each set, circle 10 buttons, count how many in all, and write the number.

CCSS	DoK	Item Number	Last Name, First Name															
K.CC.A.1	1	1																
K.CC.A.2	1	2																
K.CC.A.3	2	3																
K.CC.B.4.A	1	4																
K.CC.B.4.B	2	5																
K.CC.B.4.C	2	6																
K.CC.B.5	1	7																
K.CC.C.6	2	8																
K.CC.C.7	2	9																
K.CC.C.7	2	10																
K.OA.A.3	1	11																
K.OA.A.5	1	12																
K.OA.A.2	2	13																
K.OA.A.3	2	14																
K.OA.A.4	1	15																
K.OA.A.5	1	16																
K.OA.A.5	1	17																
K.NBT.A.1	2	18																

CCSS	DoK	Item Number	Last Name, First Name												
K.NBT.A.1	1	19													
K.NBT.A.1	1	20													
K.MD.A.1	2	21													
K.MD.A.2	2	22													
K.MD.B.3	2	23													
K.G.A.1	2	24													
K.G.A.2	1	25													
K.G.A.3	1	26													
K.G.A.3	1	27													
K.G.B.4	1	28													
K.G.B.4	1	29													
K.G.B.6	2	30													

Counting and Cardinality

1 Write the missing numbers from 1 to 20.

1									
									20

2 Circle the numbers that are in counting order.

3 4 5 7

4 5 6 7

5 6 8 9

3 How many stars? Write the number.

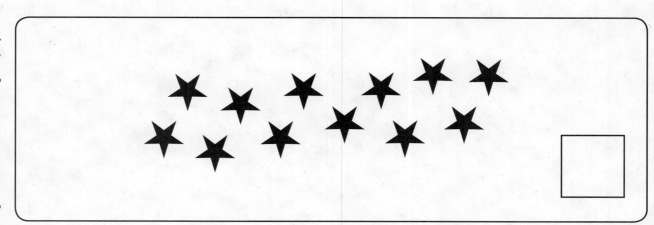

4 Circle the numbers that are in order when counting this group.

1, 2, 3, 4, 6

1, 3, 4, 5, 6

1, 2, 3, 4, 5

---

5 Circle the number you say last when counting this group.

5   6   7

6 Circle the number that comes next.

○○○
○○
5

○○○
○○○
6

○○○○
○○○
7

○○○○
○○○○
8

○○○○○
○○○○
9

---

7 Circle the group of 8 turtles.

8 Circle the group that has more.

4

6

Compare the numbers.
Write G for **Greater than** or L for **Less than**.

9

| 7 | _____ | 4 |

10

| 6 | _____ | 9 |

Operations and Algebraic Thinking

11 Write the partners.

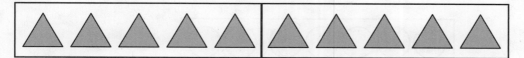

$$10 = \boxed{} + \boxed{}$$

---

12 Subtract the numbers.

$$5 - 2 = \boxed{}$$

---

13 There are 6 frogs sitting on a log.
Then 3 frogs jump into the pond. How many frogs
are still on the log? Write the equation.

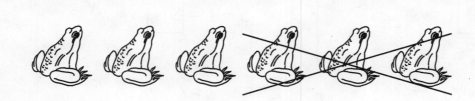

Equation: _____ – _____ = _____

14 Write the partners.

7

☐ + ☐

---

15 Write the partners.

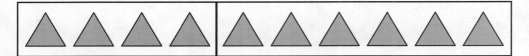

10 = ☐ + ☐

---

16 Add the numbers.

3 + 1 = ☐

17 Subtract the numbers.

5 − 4 = ☐

Number and Operations in Base Ten

 Circle a group of 10. Write how many in all.

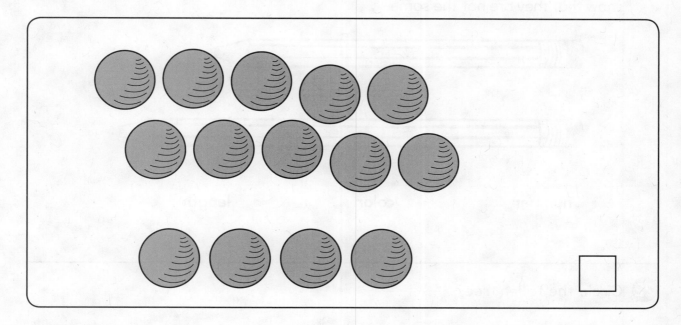

Write the total.

$$10 + 4 = \boxed{}$$

20

$$\boxed{} = 10 + 7$$

Measurement and Data

21 Circle the word that tells how the pencils could be compared to show that they are not the same.

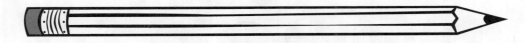

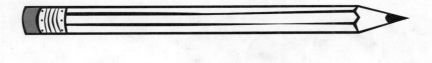

number   color   length

---

22 Circle the taller tree.

---

23 Count the triangles and the squares.
Circle the number that is more.

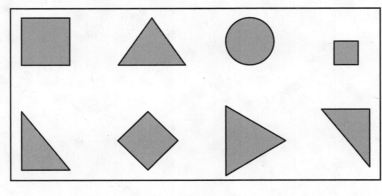

Geometry

24 Circle the cylinder that is next to the cone.

---

25 Circle the hexagon.

---

26 Circle the solid shape.

---

27 Circle the flat shape.

28 Circle the shape that is like the first shape.

 |

29 Circle the shape that is shaped like a baseball.

 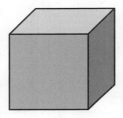

30 Adam stacks two cubes.

Circle the new shape that he makes.

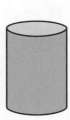 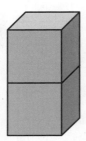

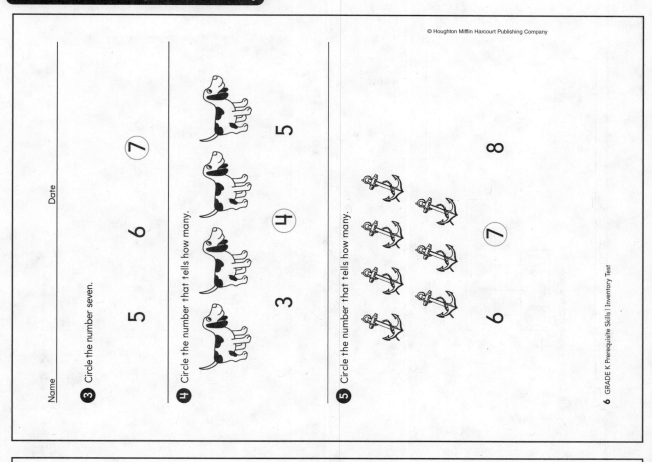

Name _____ Date _____

Prerequisite Skills Inventory Test

Counting and Cardinality

1 Count the tiger cubs.

Circle how many.

3   4   ⑤

2 Count the eggs in the nest.

Circle how many.

4   ③   2

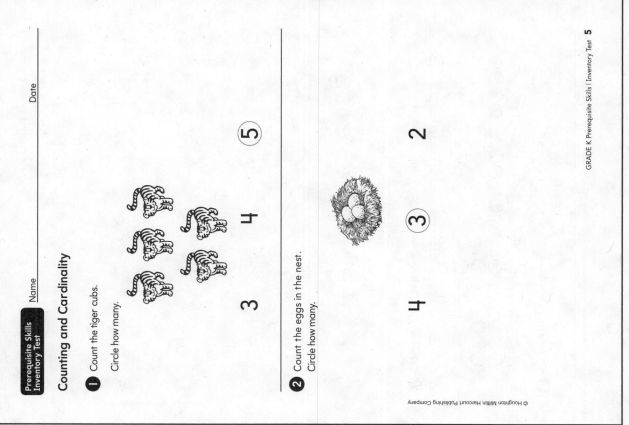

Name _____ Date _____

3 Circle the number seven.

5   6   ⑦

4 Circle the number that tells how many.

3   ④   5

5 Circle the number that tells how many.

6   ⑦   8

Name

Date

8 Circle the group that has more.

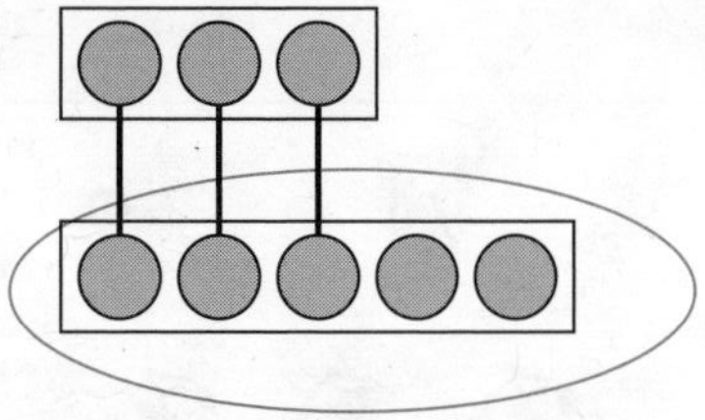

9 Count each group.
Circle the group that has less.

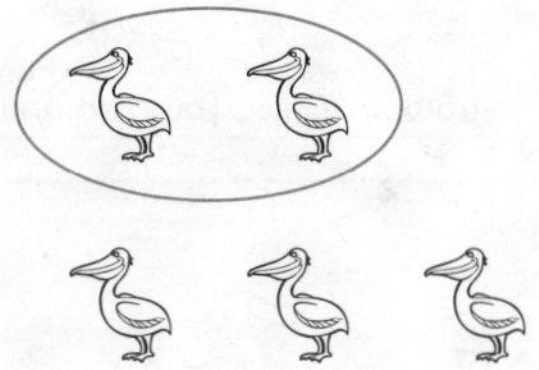

Name

Date

6 Circle the groups of 9 dots.

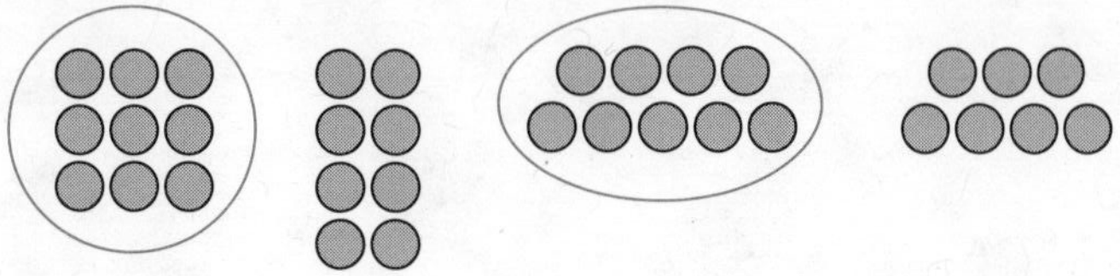

7 Circle the groups of 4 dots.

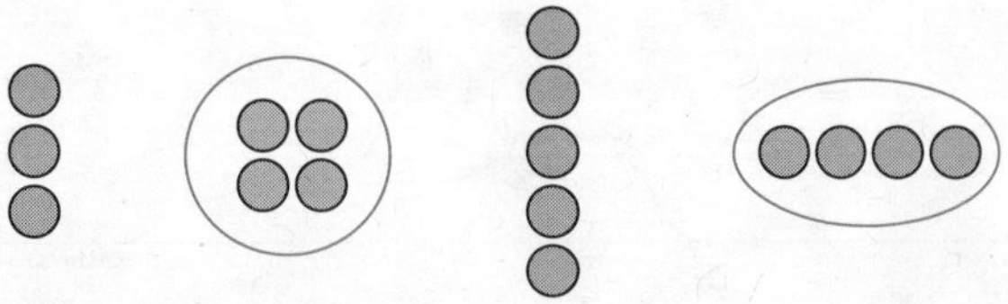

Name _____ Date _____

Operations and Algebraic Thinking

10 Circle the group that has one more apple.

11 How many kittens in all?
Write the number.

4

Name _____ Date _____

12 How many circles in all?
Write the number.

4

13 Circle the group that has one less frog.

14 Count and circle the number that is less.

5

3

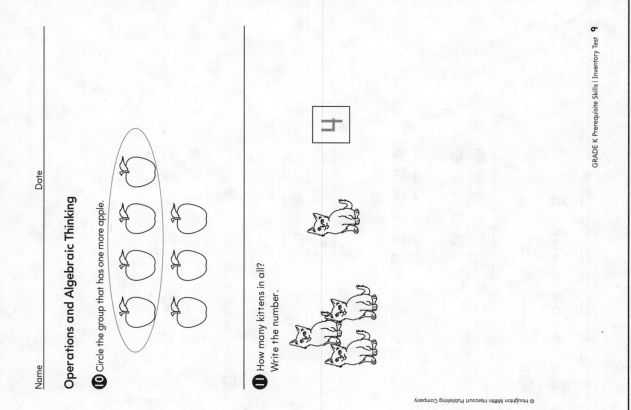

Measurement and Data

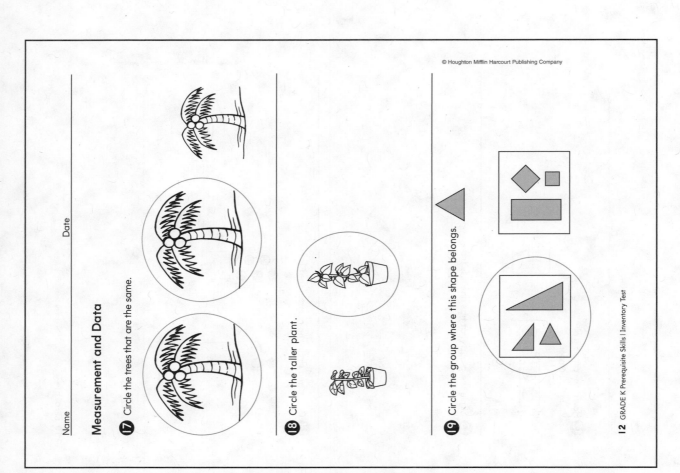

17 Circle the trees that are the same.

18 Circle the taller plant.

19 Circle the group where this shape belongs.

Number and Operations in Base Ten

15 Circle the group that shows 10.

16 Draw extra dots to show 10.

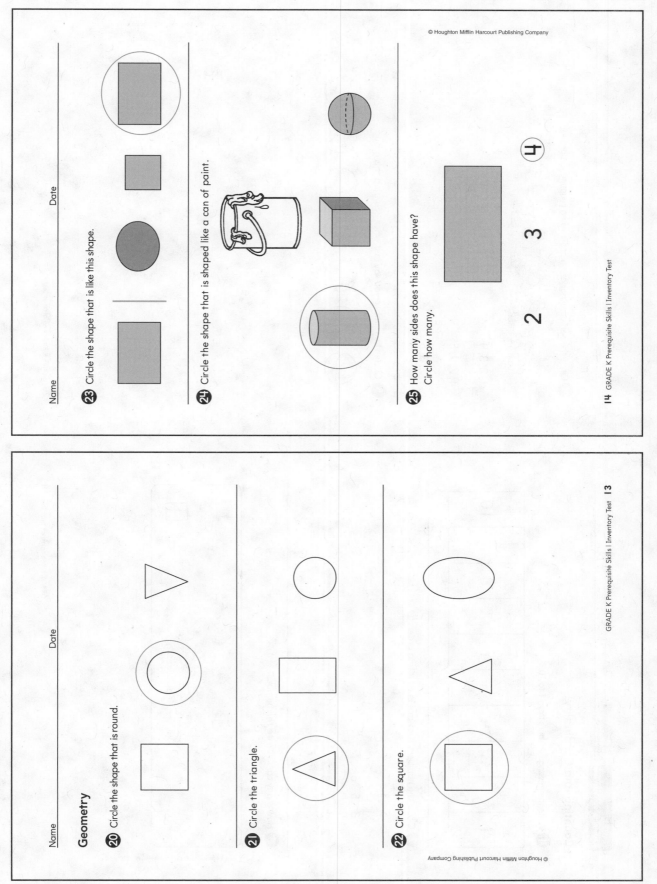

Name _____ Date _____

Geometry

20 Circle the shape that is round.

21 Circle the triangle.

22 Circle the square.

Name _____ Date _____

23 Circle the shape that is like this shape.

24 Circle the shape that is shaped like a can of paint.

25 How many sides does this shape have?
Circle how many.

2   3   4

© Houghton Mifflin Harcourt Publishing Company

Name _____ Date _____

4 Circle the numbers that are in order when counting this group.

(1, 2, 3, 4)

1, 2, 4, 5

1, 2, 3, 5

5 Circle the number you say last when counting this group.

5

6

(7)

20 GRADE K Beginning of Year Test

Grade K
Beginning of Year Test   Name _____ Date _____

Counting and Cardinality

1 Write the missing numbers from 1 to 10.

| 1 | 2 | 3 | 4 | 5 | 6 | 7 | 8 | 9 | 10 |

2 Circle the numbers that are in counting order.

1 5 3 7

4 3 5 6

(2 3 4 5)

3 How many cars? Write the number.

9

© Houghton Mifflin Harcourt Publishing Company

GRADE K Beginning of Year Test 19

Name _____ Date _____

8 Circle the group that has more.

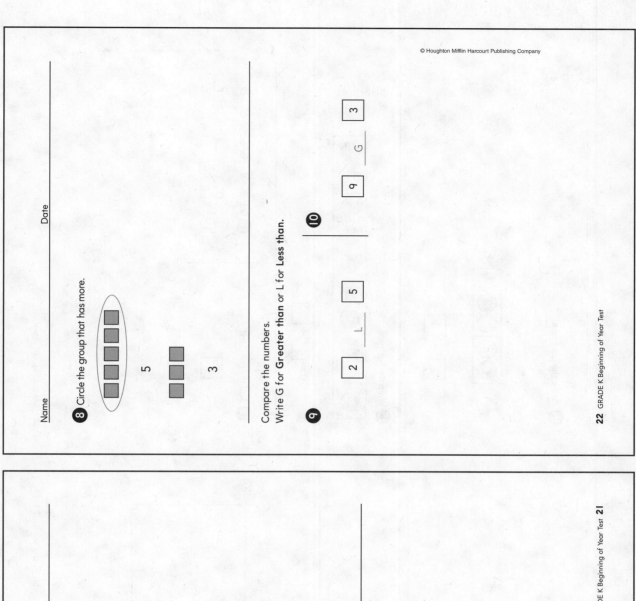

Compare the numbers.
Write G for **Greater than** or L for **Less than**.

9 | 2 | L | 5 |

10 | 9 | G | 3 |

Name _____ Date _____

6 Circle the number that comes next.

7 Circle the group of 6 cats.

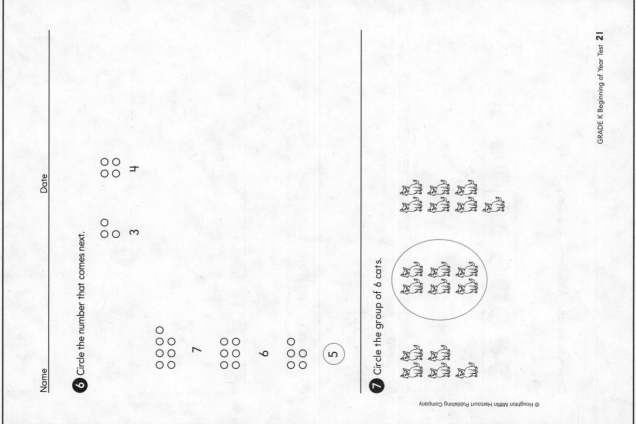

Page 24

Name _____ Date _____

14 Write the partners.

5

[2 | 3]

2 + 3

15 Write the partners.

10 = 8 + 2

16 Add the numbers.

2 + 2 = 4

17 Subtract the numbers.

4 − 1 = 3

Page 23

Name _____ Date _____

Operations and Algebraic Thinking

11 Write the partners.

10 = 7 + 3

12 Subtract the numbers.

4 − 2 = 2

13 There are 4 butterflies on a bush. Then 3 butterflies fly away. How many butterflies are left on the bush? Write the equation.

Equation: 4 − 3 = 1

Name _____ Date _____

Number and Operations in Base Ten

18 Circle a group of 10. Write how many in all.

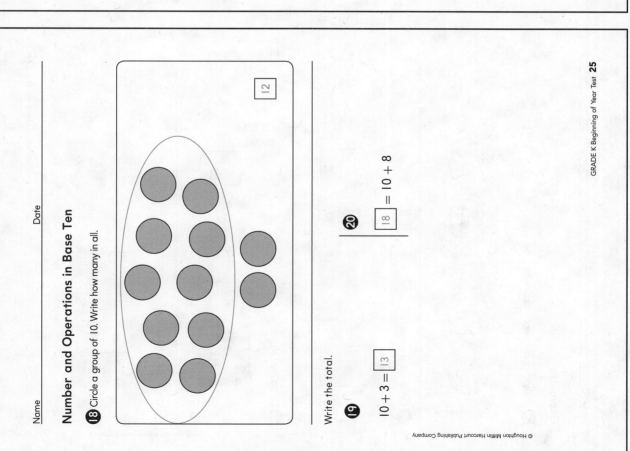

12

Write the total.

19 $10 + 3 =$ 13

20 $\underline{18} = 10 + 8$

Name _____ Date _____

Measurement and Data

21 Circle the word that tells how the branches could be compared to show that they are not the same.

distance   length   time

22 Circle the shorter tree.

23 Count the squares and circles. Circle the number that is more.

3   4

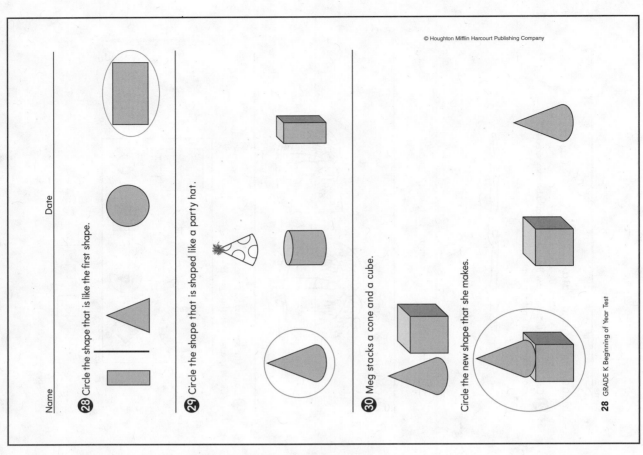

Name _____ Date _____

28 Circle the shape that is like the first shape.

29 Circle the shape that is shaped like a party hat.

30 Meg stacks a cone and a cube.

Circle the new shape that she makes.

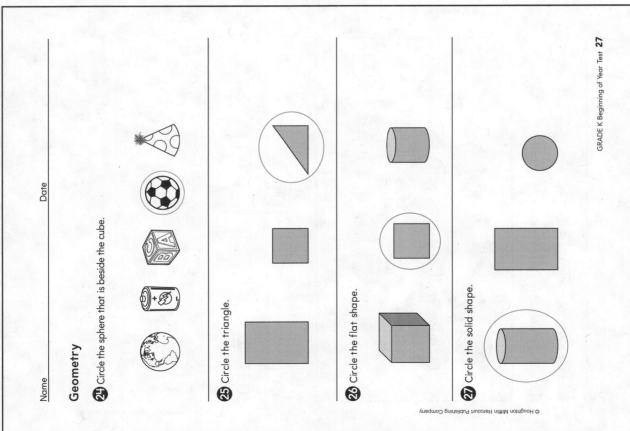

Name _____ Date _____

Geometry

24 Circle the sphere that is beside the cube.

25 Circle the triangle.

26 Circle the flat shape.

27 Circle the solid shape.

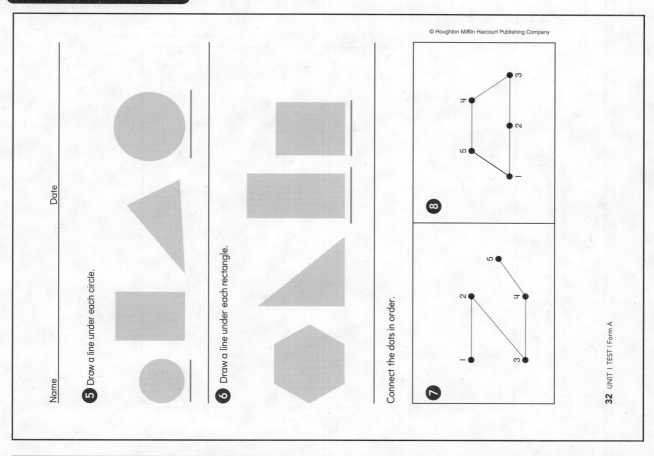

Name _____ Date _____

Unit I Test
Form A

5 Draw a line under each circle.

6 Draw a line under each rectangle.

Connect the dots in order.

7

8

32 UNIT I TEST | Form A

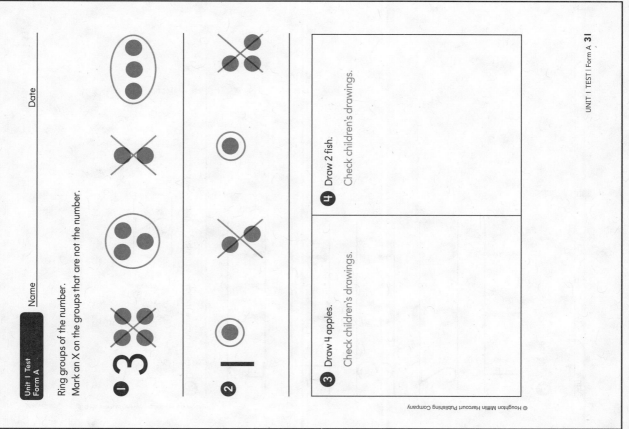

Name _____ Date _____

Unit I Test
Form A

Ring groups of the number.
Mark an X on the groups that are not the number.

I 3

2

3 Draw 4 apples.
Check children's drawings.

4 Draw 2 fish.
Check children's drawings.

UNIT I TEST | Form A **31**

Name _____ Date _____

11 Make a drawing. Use 1 rectangle, 2 squares, and 4 circles. Did you draw fewer rectangles or squares? Mark an X on the shape that has fewer.

Check children's work. Drawings will vary.

Name _____ Date _____

9 Write the numbers.

1 1 1

2 2 2

3 3 3

4 4 4

5 5 5

10 Does the picture match the number? Choose Yes or No.

2

● Yes   ○ No

Name _____ Date _____

4 Which shape is a circle?

○ ● ○ (pentagon)   ○ (square)   ● (circle)

5 Which shows the dots connected in order?

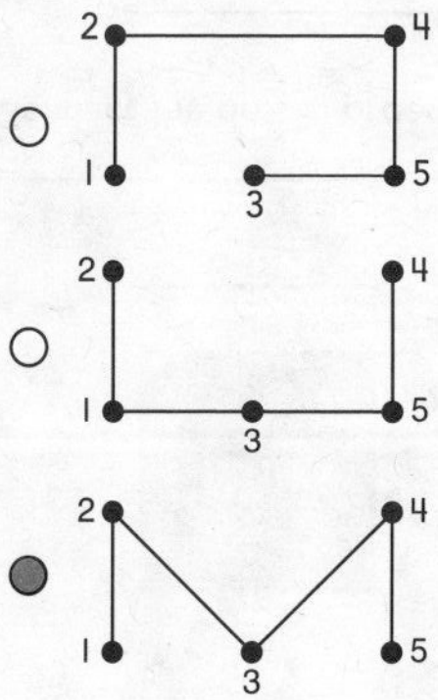

○   ○   ●

Unit 1 Test
Form B

Name _____ Date _____

Fill in the ○ for the correct answer.

Which group shows the number?

1 5   ○   ●   ○

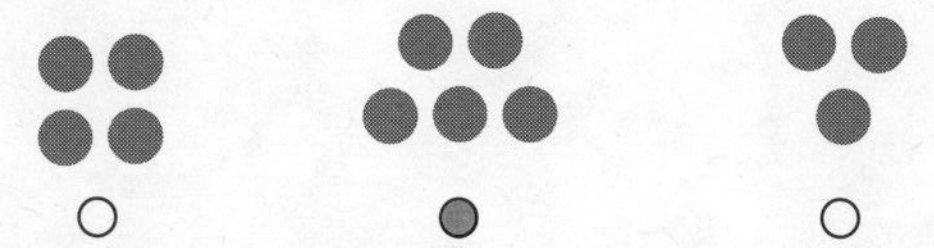

2 4   ●   ○   ○

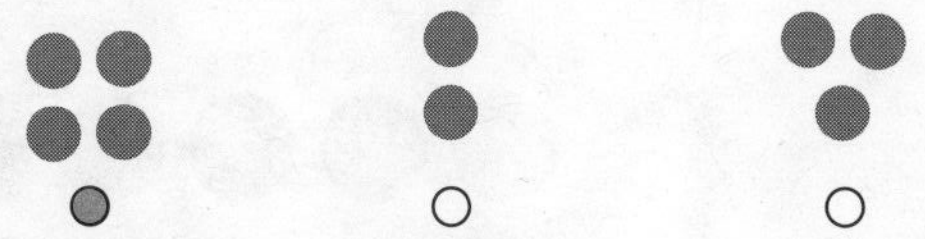

3 Which group shows 5 pails?

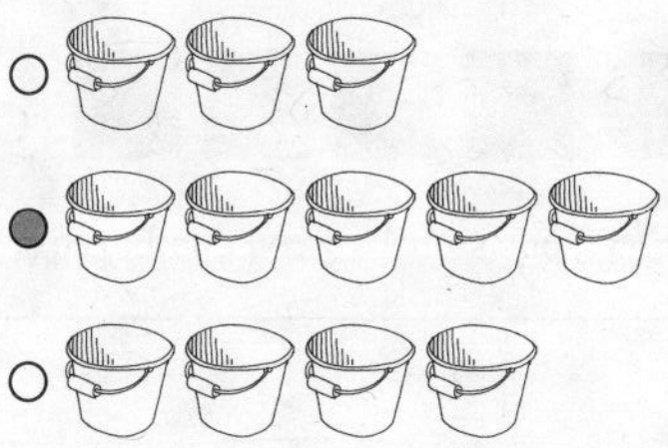

○   ●   ○

Name _____ Date _____

8 Draw 2 buttons.

Check children's drawings.

9 Draw a line under each square.

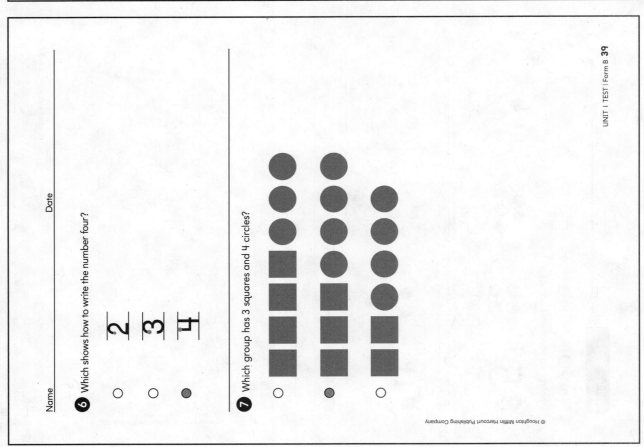

10 Connect the dots in order.

Name _____ Date _____

6 Which shows how to write the number four?

2   3   4

○   ○   ●

7 Which group has 3 squares and 4 circles?

○   ●   ○

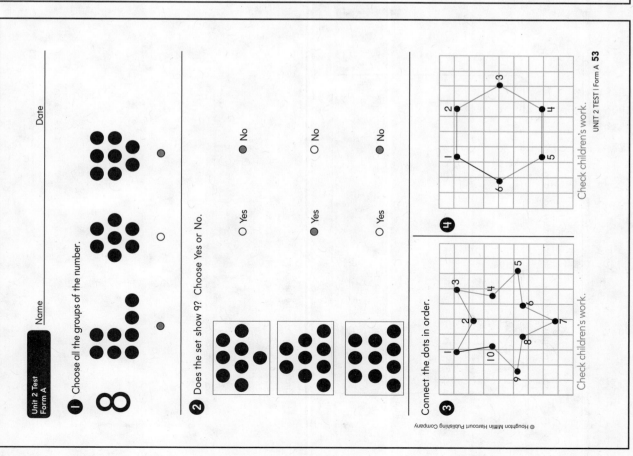

© Houghton Mifflin Harcourt Publishing Company

Name _____ **Date** _____

5 Ring the 5-group. Count the total. Write the number.

Check children's work.

$5 + 4 = 9$

6 There are 8 circles. Draw a set of circles that shows 8 – 1.
Check children's work.

Ring the number that completes the number sentence.

$8 - 1 =$

6   (7)   8

54 UNIT 2 TEST | Form A

© Houghton Mifflin Harcourt Publishing Company

Unit 2 Test Form A

Name _____ **Date** _____

1 Choose all the groups of the number.

8

2 Does the set show 9? Choose Yes or No.

○ Yes   ● No

● Yes   ○ No

○ Yes   ● No

3 Connect the dots in order.

Check children's work.

4

Check children's work.

UNIT 2 TEST | Form A **53**

Name _____ Date _____

7 Draw 3 triangles in the box. Write how many sides a triangle has.

Check children's work.

A triangle has ___3___ sides.

8 Draw a line under the hexagons.

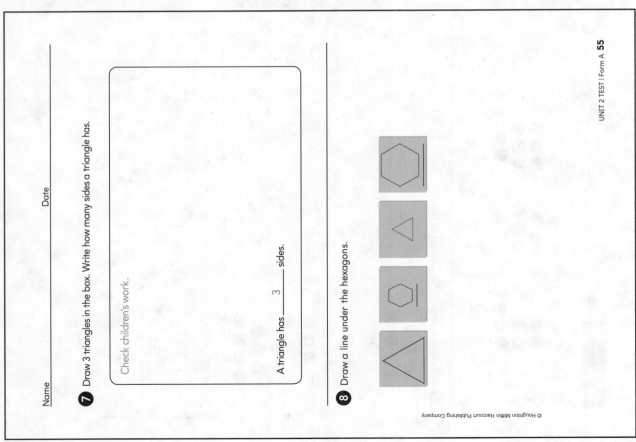

Name _____ Date _____

9 Look at the number tiles. Write the numbers 6 through 10 in order.

6   8   7   9   10

| 5 | 6 | 7 | 8 | 9 | 10 |

10 Draw a picture that shows 7 + 1 squares. Write how many squares.

Children's drawings should show a group of 7 squares and 1 square.

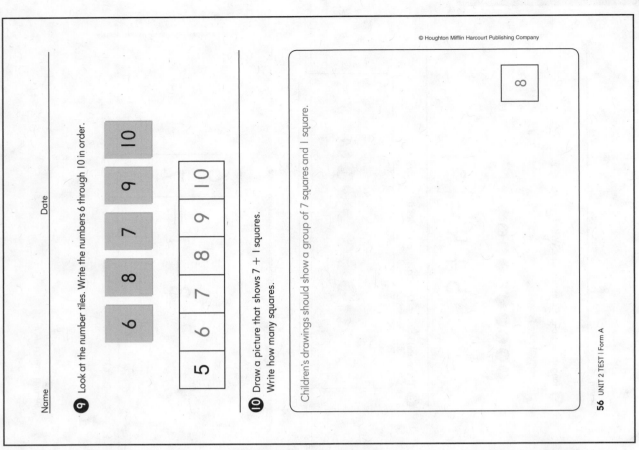

8

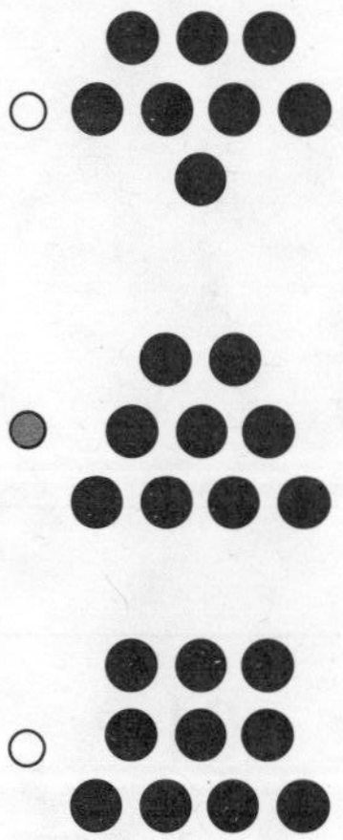

© Houghton Mifflin Harcourt Publishing Company

Name _____ Date _____

Unit 2 Test Form B

Fill in the ◯ for the correct answer.

1 Which group shows the number?

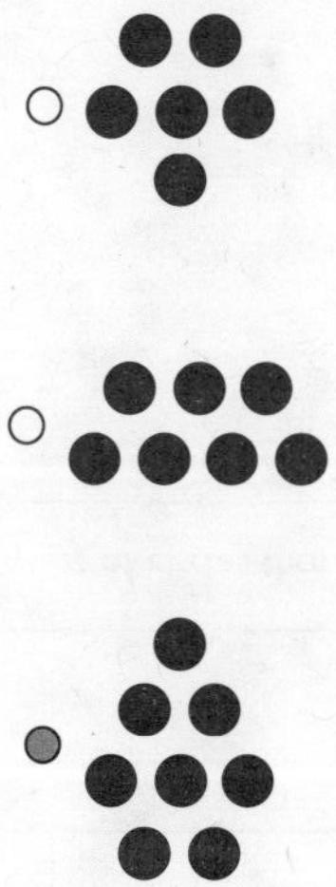

8

2

9

UNIT 2 TEST | Form B **59**

Name _____ Date _____

3 Which shows the dots connected in order?

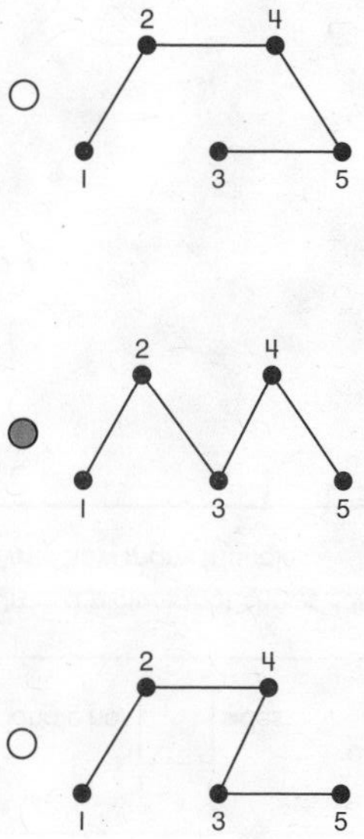

4

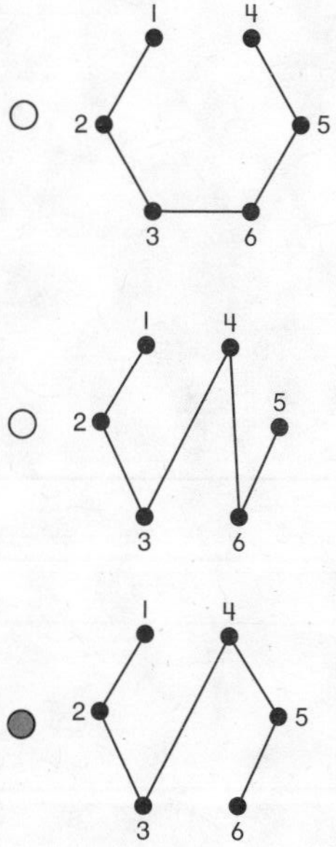

5 The 5-group is circled. Count the total. Which shows the number?

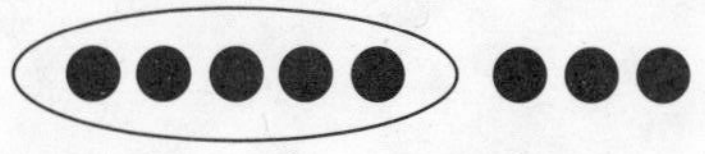

◯ 8   ◯ 9   ◯ 10

Name _____ Date _____

9 Draw 2 triangles in the box. Write how many sides a triangle has.

Check children's work.

A triangle has $\boxed{3}$ sides.

10 Draw a picture that shows 8 + 1 triangles. Write how many triangles.

Children's drawings should show a group of 8 triangles and 1 triangle.

$\boxed{9}$

Name _____ Date _____

6 Which shape is a hexagon?

○   ○   ●

7 Which number is missing from 5 to 10?

| 5 | 6 | 7 | 8 | 10 |

○ 7   ● 9   ○ 10

8 Draw a set of circles that shows 7 – 1.

Check children's work.

© Houghton Mifflin Harcourt Publishing Company

Name _____ Date _____

6 Choose all the partners that are equal to 6.

5 Write each number. Ring = or ≠.

⊙⊙⊙
⊙⊙⊙   ⊙⊙
⊙⊙⊙   ⊙⊙
            ⊙⊙

| 6 | Ⓔ= ≠ | 6 |

7 Add the numbers. Ring the answer.

2 + 1 = 3 | Ⓘ | 2 | ③ |

8 Subtract the numbers. Ring the answer.

3 − 2 = 1 | ① | 2 | 3 |

© Houghton Mifflin Harcourt Publishing Company

Name _____ Date _____

Write the partners.

1 7
6 + 1

2 7
3 + 4

3 Ring a group of 10. Count all of the baseballs. Write how many in all.

16

4 Ring the number. Draw it using the 5-group.

6 ⑦ 8

© Houghton Mifflin Harcourt Publishing Company

Name _____ Date _____

Use the pictures below to complete Exercises 9–12.

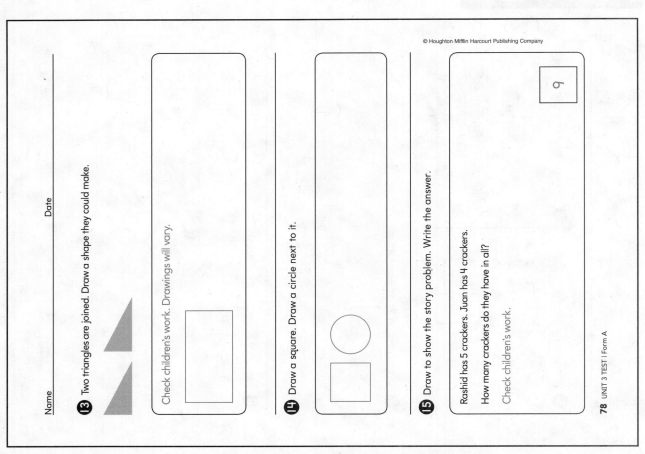

9 Ring all of the three-sided shapes.

10 How many triangles are there?
○ 3   ○ 4   ● 5

11 How many rectangles are there?
○ 3   ● 4   ○ 5

12 Are there more triangles or rectangles? Ring the shape with more.

Name _____ Date _____

13 Two triangles are joined. Draw a shape they could make.

Check children's work. Drawings will vary.

14 Draw a square. Draw a circle next to it.

15 Draw to show the story problem. Write the answer.

Rashid has 5 crackers. Juan has 4 crackers.
How many crackers do they have in all?

Check children's work.

9

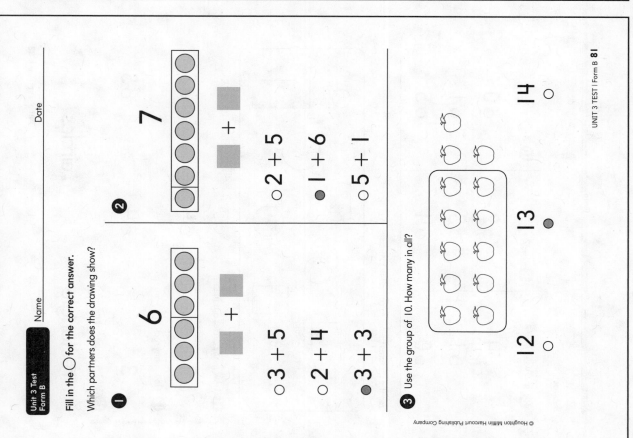

© Houghton Mifflin Harcourt Publishing Company

Name _____ **Date** _____

4 Two triangles are joined. Which new shape could they make?

Add.

5 3 + 2 =
○ 1
○ 4
● 5

6 2 + 1 =
○ 1
○ 2
● 3

7 3 + 1 =
● 4
○ 2
○ 1

© Houghton Mifflin Harcourt Publishing Company

Name _____ **Date** _____

Unit 3 Test
Form B

Fill in the ○ for the correct answer.

Which partners does the drawing show?

1
6

○ 3 + 5
○ 2 + 4
● 3 + 3

2
7

○ 2 + 5
● 1 + 6
○ 5 + 1

3 Use the group of 10. How many in all?

○ 12
● 13
○ 14

© Houghton Mifflin Harcourt Publishing Company

Name

Date

14 Which equation does the drawing show?

- ● $17 = 10 + 7$
- ○ $16 = 10 + 6$
- ○ $15 = 10 + 5$

15 Which describes the shapes in the drawing?

- ● A circle is below a square.
- ○ A triangle is above a circle.
- ○ A circle is above a square.

Name

Date

Subtract.

8 $4 - 4 =$
- ○ 4
- ○ 1
- ● 0

9 $4 - 2 =$
- ● 2
- ○ 3
- ○ 4

10 $3 - 2 =$
- ○ 0
- ● 1
- ○ 5

Use the pictures below to complete Exercises 11–13.

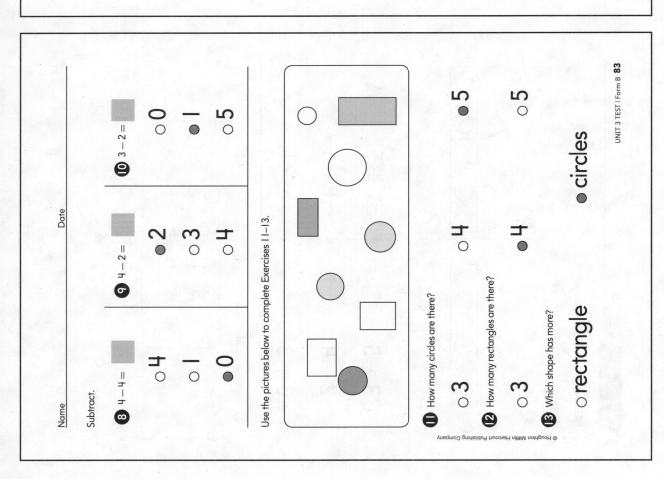

11 How many circles are there?
- ○ 3
- ○ 4
- ● 5

12 How many rectangles are there?
- ● 3
- ○ 4
- ○ 5

13 Which shape has more?
- ○ rectangle
- ● circles

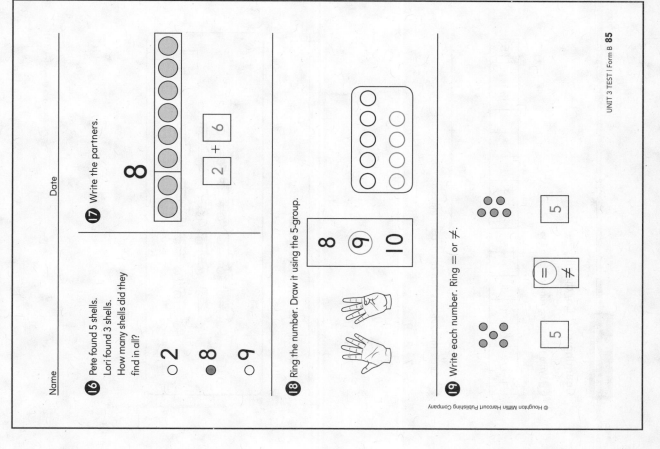

Name _____ Date _____

16 Pete found 5 shells.
Lori found 3 shells.
How many shells did they
find in all?

○ 2
● 8
○ 9

17 Write the partners.

8

| 2 | + | 6 |

18 Ring the number. Draw it using the 5-group.

8
⑨
10

19 Write each number. Ring = or ≠.

| 5 | | 5 |

(=)   ≠

Name _____ Date _____

4 Circle the numbers that are in order when counting this group.

🍎🍎🍎🍎🍎

(1, 2, 3, 4, 5)

1, 3, 4, 5, 6

1, 2, 3, 5, 6

5 Circle the number you say last when counting this group.

7   (8)   9

Grade K
Middle of Year Test

Name _____ Date _____

Counting and Cardinality

1 Write the missing numbers from 1 to 15.

1	2	3	4	5	6	7	8	9	10	11	12	13	14	15

2 Circle the numbers that are in counting order.

(6 7 8 9)

6 8 9 10

5 7 9 10

3 How many trucks? Write the number.

12

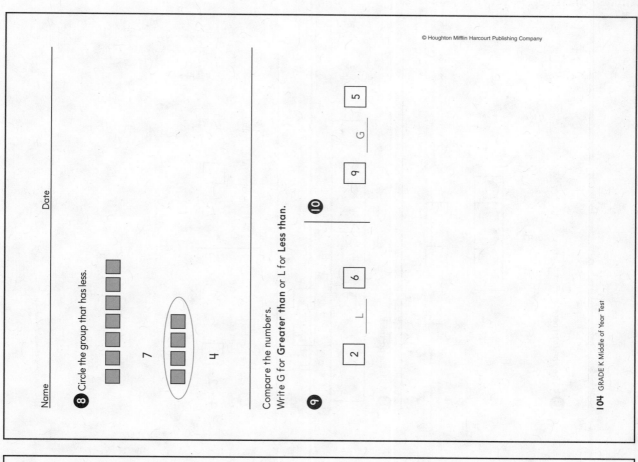

Name _____ Date _____

8 Circle the group that has less.

7

4

9 Compare the numbers.
Write G for **Greater than** or L for **Less than.**

| 2 | L | 6 |

10 | 9 | G | 5 |

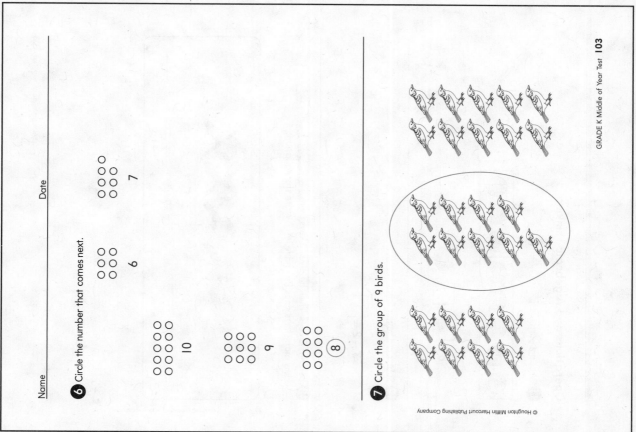

Name _____ Date _____

6 Circle the number that comes next.

6

7

10

9

⑧

7 Circle the group of 9 birds.

Name _____ Date _____

Operations and Algebraic Thinking

11 Write the partners.

$8 = 5 + 3$

12 Subtract the numbers.

$3 - 2 = 1$

13 Ben has 5 keys. Then he gives 2 keys away. How many keys does Ben have left? Write the equation.

Equation: $5 - 2 = 3$

Name _____ Date _____

14 Write the partners. 5

$4 + 1$

15 Write the partners.

$10 = 6 + 4$

16 Add the numbers.

$1 + 2 = 3$

17 Subtract the numbers.

$4 - 1 = 3$

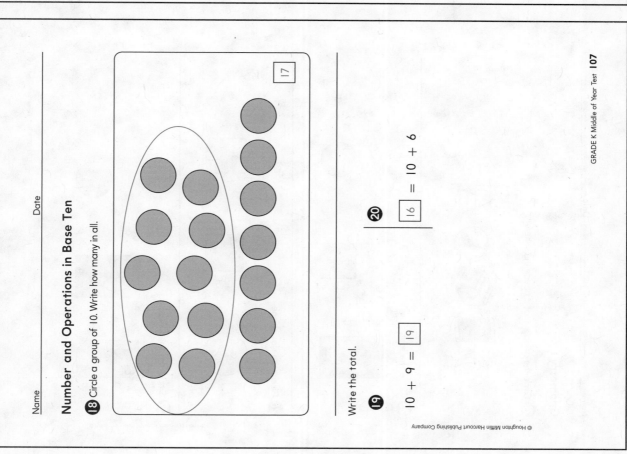

Name _____ Date _____

Measurement and Data

21 Circle the word that tells how the pens could be compared to show that they are not the same.

distance   length   time

22 Circle the taller light.

23 Count the squares and circles. Circle the number that is more.

4   5

Name _____ Date _____

Number and Operations in Base Ten

18 Circle a group of 10. Write how many in all.

17

Write the total.

19 $10 + 9 =$ 19

20 16 $= 10 + 6$

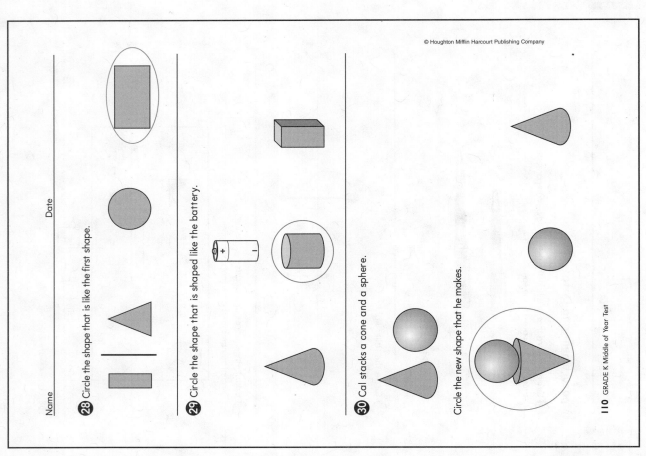

Name _____ Date _____

28 Circle the shape that is like the first shape.

29 Circle the shape that is shaped like the battery.

30 Cal stacks a cone and a sphere.

Circle the new shape that he makes.

Name _____ Date _____

Geometry

24 Circle the cylinder that is beside the sphere.

25 Circle the square.

26 Circle the flat shape.

27 Circle the solid shape.

Name _____ Date _____

Add. Ring the answer.

4 1 + 4 = [3] (5)

Count and write the number. Ring the number that is less.

6 (2) [4]

Subtract. Ring the answer.

5 3 − 0 = 0 (3)

7 3 [2]

Draw lines to match the equation to the drawing.

8 10 + 4 = 14   10 + 3 = 13   10 + 1 = 11

**Unit 4 Test
Form A**

Name _____ Date _____

1 **Count to find how many suns. Write the partners.**

10 = [8] + [2]

2 **Rick has 8 oranges. He eats 2 oranges.
Draw the oranges Rick has left.**

Children's drawings show 6 oranges.

3 **Which partner of 10 does the picture show?**

○ 10 = 4 + 6
● 10 = 7 + 3
○ 10 = 9 + 1

Name _____ Date _____

14 Ring the cube that is next to the cylinder.

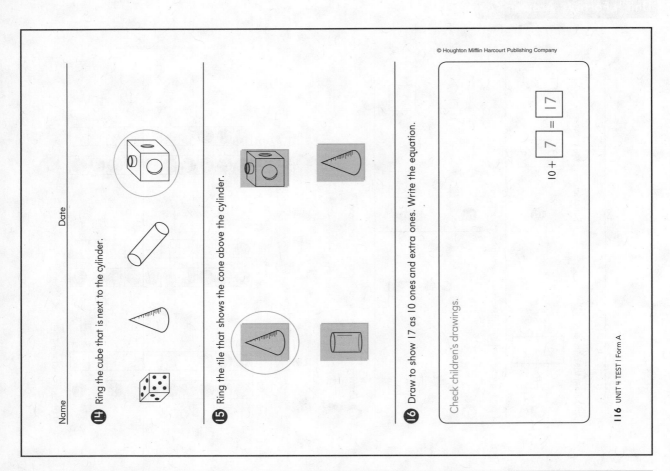

15 Ring the tile that shows the cone above the cylinder.

16 Draw to show 17 as 10 ones and extra ones. Write the equation.

Check children's drawings.

$10 + 7 = 17$

Name _____ Date _____

9 Choose all of the pictures that are solid shapes.

Use the pictures below to complete Exercises 10–13.

10 How many spheres are there? 3

11 How many cylinders are there? 3

12 How many cones are there? 2

13 How many cubes are there? 2

© Houghton Mifflin Harcourt Publishing Company

Name _____ **Date** _____

Fill in the ○ for the correct answer.

Which partners does the drawing show?

1 🌼🌼🌼🌼🌼🌼🌼🌼🌼🌼

● $10 = 6 + 4$
○ $10 = 7 + 3$
○ $10 = 8 + 2$

2 🌼🌼🌼🌼🌼🌼🌼🌼🌼🌼

○ $10 = 5 + 5$
○ $10 = 6 + 4$
● $10 = 7 + 3$

Add the numbers.

3 $5 + 0 =$ ▨

○ 0
● 5
○ 6

4 $1 + 4 =$ ▨

○ 3
○ 4
● 5

5 $3 + 1 =$ ▨

○ 2
● 4
○ 5

Subtract the numbers.

6 $3 - 0 =$ ▨

○ 0
● 3
○ 4

7 $4 - 2 =$ ▨

● 2
○ 3
○ 6

8 $5 - 1 =$ ▨

○ 6
○ 5
● 4

© Houghton Mifflin Harcourt Publishing Company

Name _____ **Date** _____

Which partners does the drawing show?

9 ❄❄❄❄❄❄

○ $7 = 5 + 2$
● $7 = 6 + 1$
○ $7 = 7 + 0$

10 ❄❄❄❄❄❄❄❄

○ $8 = 3 + 5$
○ $8 = 2 + 7$
● $8 = 2 + 6$

Complete the equation.

11 $10 + 5 =$ ▨

● 15
○ 14
○ 13

12 $10 + 6 =$ ▨

○ 14
○ 15
● 16

Name _____ Date _____

16 Which equation does the drawing show?

○ $10 + 3 = 13$

● $10 + 2 = 12$

○ $10 + 1 = 11$

Add the numbers.

17 $1 + 3 =$

● 4

○ 3

○ 1

18 $3 + 2 =$

○ 1

○ 4

● 5

Name _____ Date _____

13 Which is a cylinder?

○   ● (cylinder)   ○

14 Which is a sphere?

○   ○   ● (globe)

15 Which is true about the cylinder?

○ It is above the cone.

○ It is behind the cone.

● It is in front of the cone.

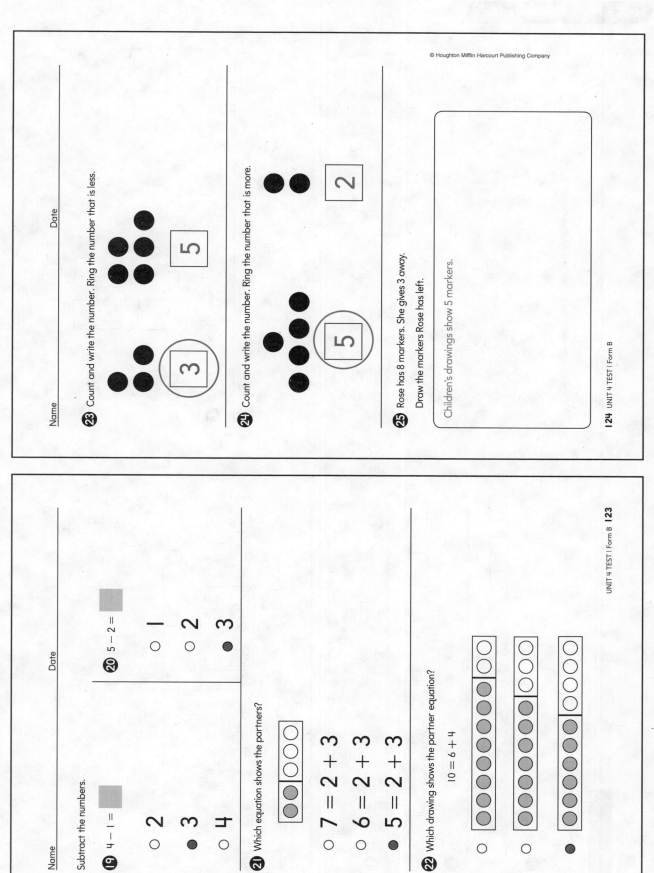

Name

Date

Subtract the numbers.

19 4 − 1 =

○ 2
● 3
○ 4

20 5 − 2 =

○ 1
○ 2
● 3

21 Which equation shows the partners?

○ 7 = 2 + 3
○ 6 = 2 + 3
● 5 = 2 + 3

22 Which drawing shows the partner equation?

10 = 6 + 4

○
○
●

Name

Date

23 Count and write the number. Ring the number that is less.

3   5

24 Count and write the number. Ring the number that is more.

5   2

25 Rose has 8 markers. She gives 3 away. Draw the markers Rose has left.

Children's drawings show 5 markers.

Unit 5 Form B Answer Key

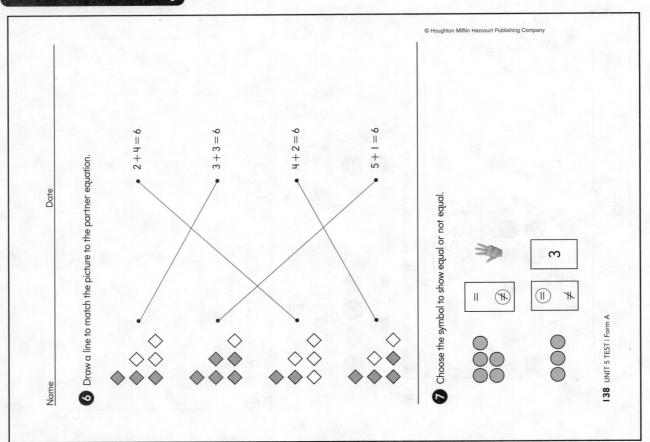

6 Draw a line to match the picture to the partner equation.

$2 + 4 = 6$

$3 + 3 = 6$

$4 + 2 = 6$

$5 + 1 = 6$

7 Choose the symbol to show equal or not equal.

138 UNIT 5 TEST | Form A

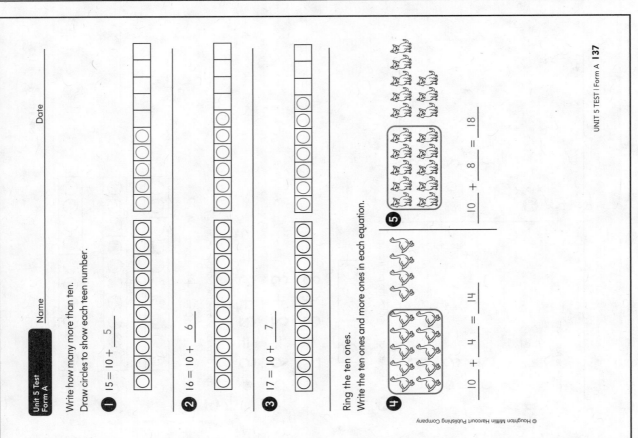

Unit 5 Test Form A

Write how many more than ten.
Draw circles to show each teen number.

1 $15 = 10 + \underline{5}$

2 $16 = 10 + \underline{6}$

3 $17 = 10 + \underline{7}$

Ring the ten ones.
Write the ten ones and more ones in each equation.

4 $10 + 4 = 14$

5 $10 + 8 = 18$

UNIT 5 TEST | Form A **137**

Name _____ Date _____

8 Write the numbers and compare them. Write **G** for **Greater** and **L** for **Less**. Cross out to make the groups equal.

| 6 | L |
| 10 | G |

Draw Tiny Tumblers on the Math Mountain and write the equation partners. Complete the equation.

9 10

$6 + 4 = 10$

10 10

$2 + 8 = 10$

Use the numbers on the tiles to complete the equations.

| 6 | 7 | 8 | 9 | 10 |

11 $8 + 1 = \boxed{9}$

12 $7 + 3 = \boxed{10}$

13 $6 + 2 = \boxed{8}$

Name _____ Date _____

14 Choose the heavier object.

15 Draw a short flower and a tall flower. Ring the shorter one.

Check children's drawings. Drawings will vary.

16 Draw to solve. Then write the equation.
There are 9 children playing at the park.
Then 2 of them go home.
How many children are still at the park?

Children's drawings show 7 children.

Equation: $\underline{9} - \underline{2} = \underline{7}$

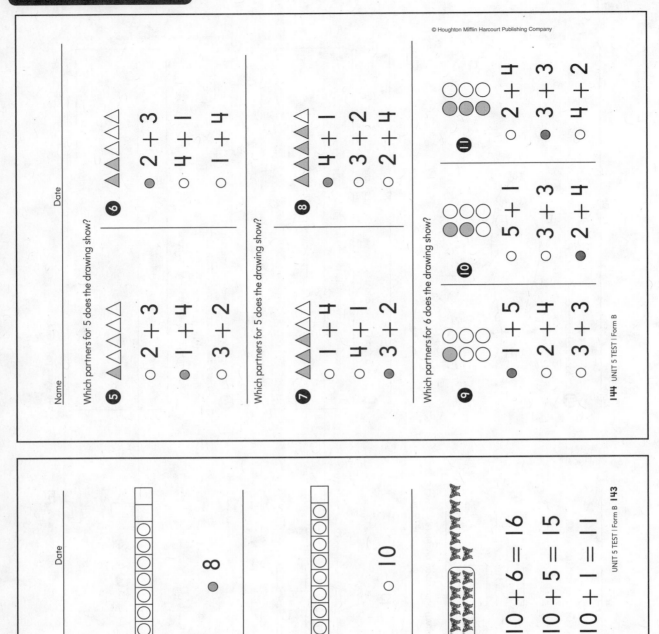

Name

Date

20 Which shows the correct way to compare the numbers?

| 7 | L |
| 5 | G |

○

| 7 | G |
| 5 | L |

●

| 7 | G |
| 4 | L |

○

21 Choose the object that is longer.

○   ●

Name

Date

Which partners for 6 does the drawing show?

12

○ 1 + 5
○ 3 + 3
● 4 + 2

13

○ 3 + 3
○ 4 + 2
● 5 + 1

Add.

14 3 + 2 =
○ 4
● 5
○ 6

15 2 + 1 =
○ 2
● 3
○ 4

16 1 + 3 =
○ 2
○ 3
● 4

Subtract.

17 6 − 3 =
● 3
○ 4
○ 5

18 7 − 5 =
○ 1
● 2
○ 3

19 5 − 4 =
● 1
○ 2
○ 3

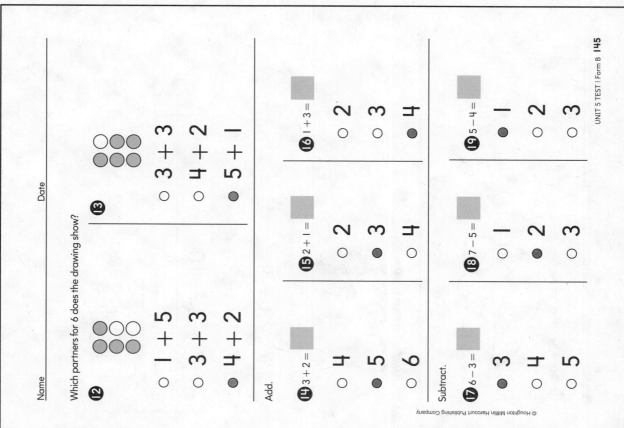

Name _____ Date _____

25 The circles show the teen number. Write how many more than ten.

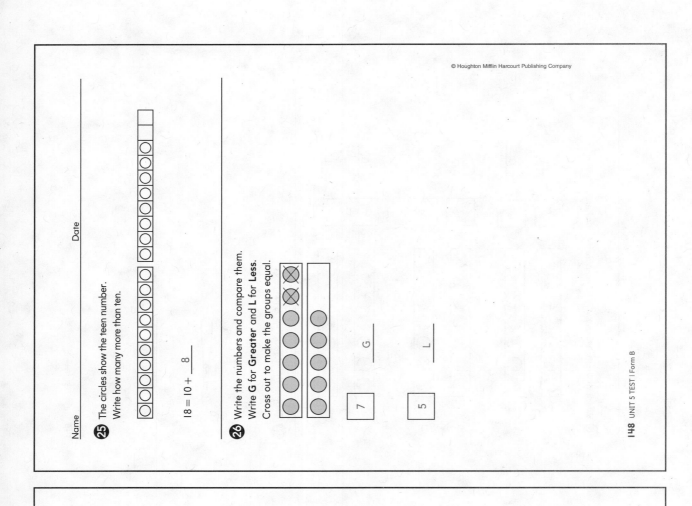

$18 = 10 + \underline{8}$

26 Write the numbers and compare them. Write **G** for **Greater** and **L** for **Less**. Cross out to make the groups equal.

7	__G__
5	__L__

Name _____ Date _____

22 Choose the animal that is lighter.

23 There are 7 markers in the box. There are 3 markers on the table. Which equation shows how many markers in all?

○ $7 - 3 = 4$

○ $7 - 4 = 3$

● $7 + 3 = 10$

24 What does the picture show? Write the numbers on the lines.

__10__ ones and __7__ ones

Name _____ Date _____

Grade K
End of Year Test

Counting and Cardinality

1 Write the missing numbers from 1 to 20.

1	2	3	4	5	6	7	8	9	10
11	12	13	14	15	16	17	18	19	20

2 Circle the numbers that are in counting order.

3 4 5 7

(4 5 6 7)

5 6 8 9

3 How many stars? Write the number.

12

GRADE K End of Year Test **163**

Name _____ Date _____

4 Circle the numbers that are in order when counting this group.

1, 2, 3, 4, 6

1, 3, 4, 5, 6

(1, 2, 3, 4, 5)

5 Circle the number you say last when counting this group.

5

(6)

7

164 GRADE K End of Year Test

Name _____ Date _____

8 Circle the group that has more.

4

6

Compare the numbers.
Write G for **Greater than** or L for **Less than**.

9

| 7 | G | 4 |

10

| 6 | L | 9 |

Name _____ Date _____

6 Circle the number that comes next.

5   6

7

8

9

7 Circle the group of 8 turtles.

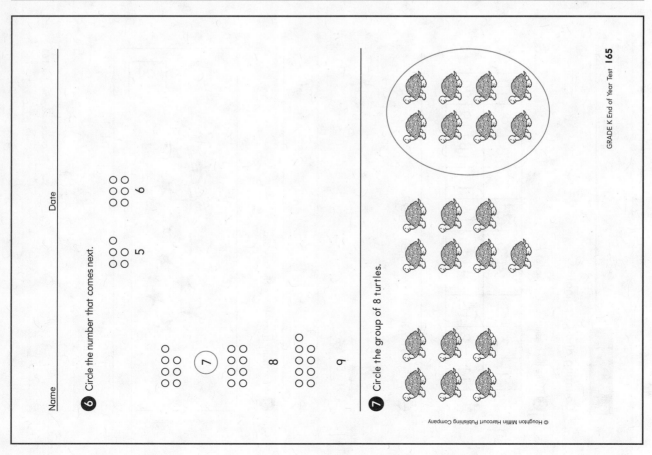

Name _____ Date _____

Operations and Algebraic Thinking

11 Write the partners.

$10 = 5 + 5$

12 Subtract the numbers.

$5 - 2 = 3$

13 There are 6 frogs sitting on a log. Then 3 frogs jump into the pond. How many frogs are still on the log? Write the equation.

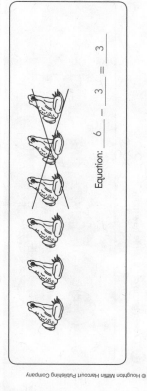

Equation: $6 - 3 = 3$

Name _____ Date _____

14 Write the partners.

7

$5 + 2$

15 Write the partners.

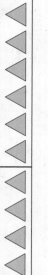

$10 = 4 + 6$

16 Add the numbers.

$3 + 1 = 4$

17 Subtract the numbers.

$5 - 4 = 1$

Name

Date

Measurement and Data

21 Circle the word that tells how the pencils could be compared to show that they are not the same.

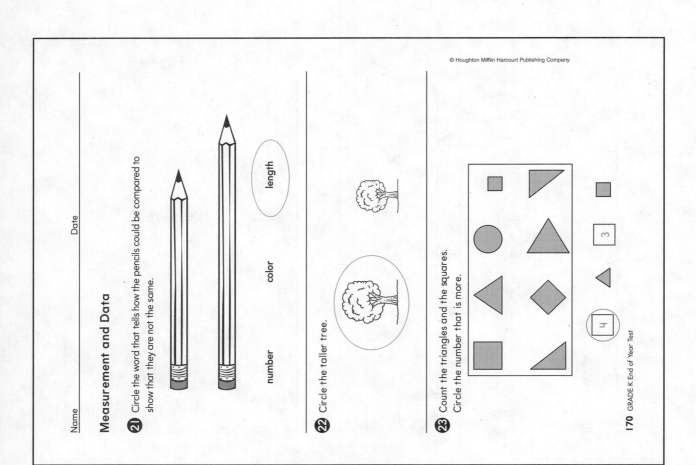

number   color   length

22 Circle the taller tree.

23 Count the triangles and the squares. Circle the number that is more.

3

4

Name

Date

Number and Operations in Base Ten

18 Circle a group of 10. Write how many in all.

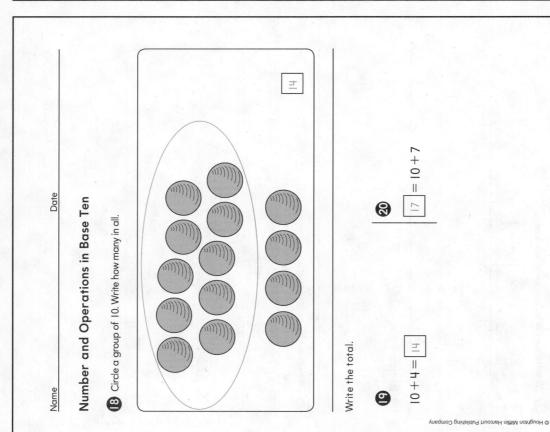

14

Write the total.

19 $10 + 4 = 14$

20 $17 = 10 + 7$

Name _____ Date _____

28 Circle the shape that is like the first shape.

29 Circle the shape that is shaped like a baseball.

30 Adam stacks two cubes.
Circle the new shape that he makes.

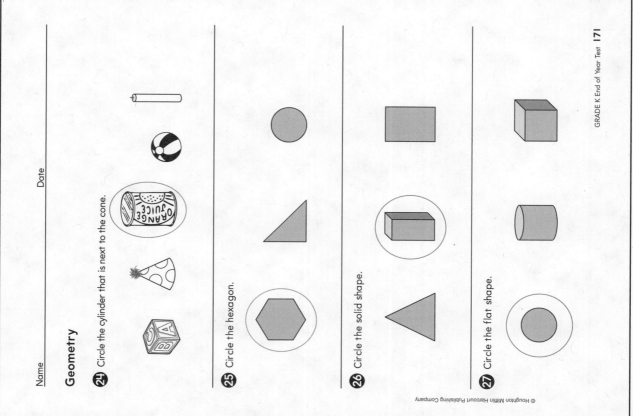

Name _____ Date _____

Geometry

24 Circle the cylinder that is next to the cone.

25 Circle the hexagon.

26 Circle the solid shape.

27 Circle the flat shape.

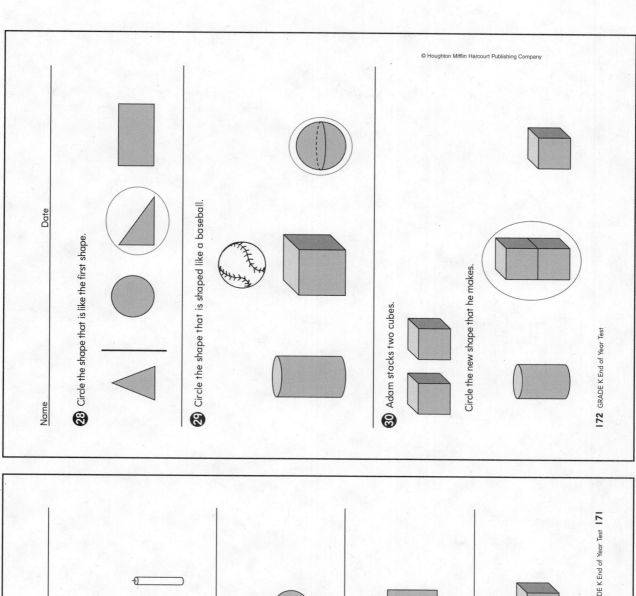

math
expressions
Common Core

Assessment Guide

Houghton
Mifflin
Harcourt™

hmhco.com

Grade K

ISBN 978-1-328-70362-0

9 781328 703620

90000

1672496